M343
Applications of probability

BOOK 1

Probability and random variables

About M343

M343 *Applications of probability* is about the application of probability to modelling real-life situations. It follows the level 2 module M248 *Analysing data* and develops ideas about probability and random processes that are introduced there. Software for exploring properties of random processes is supplied as part of M343; its use is covered in the *Computer Book*.

This publication forms part of an Open University module. Details of this and other Open University modules can be obtained from the Student Registration and Enquiry Service, The Open University, PO Box 197, Milton Keynes MK7 6BJ, United Kingdom (tel. +44 (0)845 300 60 90; email general-enquiries@open.ac.uk).

Alternatively, you may visit the Open University website at www.open.ac.uk where you can learn more about the wide range of modules and packs offered at all levels by The Open University.

To purchase a selection of Open University materials visit www.ouw.co.uk, or contact Open University Worldwide, Walton Hall, Milton Keynes MK7 6AA, United Kingdom for a brochure (tel. +44 (0)1908 858793; fax +44 (0)1908 858787; email ouw-customer-services@open.ac.uk).

Edited, designed and typeset by The Open University, using the Open University TeX System.

Printed in the United Kingdom by Hobbs the Printers Limited, Brunel Road, Totton, Hampshire SO40 3WX.

ISBN 978 1 8487 3411 1

1.1

Contents

Study guide

This book has three aims: first, to revise some basic ideas and techniques for probability and random variables with which you are assumed to be familiar (or to provide a concise introduction to any with which you are not familiar); second, to introduce a number of ideas and techniques that will be used frequently in *Books 2* to *5*; and third, to review briefly some of the mathematical results and techniques with which you are assumed to be familiar.

Many of the sections in this book depend on ideas and results from earlier sections of the book, so we recommend that you study the sections in sequential order.

This book contains both *activities*, which are included at various points in the text, and *exercises*, which are placed at the end of some sections. Their purposes are quite different. Activities form a central part of the text and you should try to do them as you work through the book. Exercises are provided to give you further practice at applying certain techniques and ideas *if you need it*: you should not routinely try them all as you study the book. You may find it more helpful to try them only if you are unsure that you have understood an idea. You will find a few further exercises in Section 9; some of these exercises cover material from more than one section. Solutions to the activities and exercises may be found at the back of this book.

This book will require nine study sessions of between $2\frac{1}{2}$ and 3 hours. The idea of a 'study session' of $2\frac{1}{2}$–3 hours has been introduced simply to help you to plan your study. This includes time for answering the TMA questions and consolidating your work on this book. You should schedule six study sessions for working through Sections 1 to 6, two for answering the TMA questions on these sections and generally consolidating your work on them, and one for working through Section 7. However, if most of the material covered is new to you, then you may need more time.

One possible study pattern is as follows.

Study session 1: Section 1.

Study session 2: Section 2.

Study session 3: Section 3.

Study session 4: Section 4.

Study session 5: Section 5.

Study session 6: Section 6.

Study sessions 7 and 8: Answering the TMA questions on this book and consolidating your work on Sections 1 to 6 of the book.

Study session 9: Section 7.

Study time has not been allocated for Sections 8 and 9. Section 8 contains a brief review of mathematical results and techniques. You should work through some or all of this section only if you are unsure of some of the techniques described there. A good way to use the section is to refer to it if and when you need to as you study M343. Section 9 contains supplementary exercises on the topics covered in Sections 1 to 6.

Introduction

Chance plays an important part in all aspects of life. We take chances every day: whether we catch the bus or just miss it; whether or not we are caught in a sudden shower; whether or not we are involved in an accident; whether a shot at goal lands in the goal or misses. Chance or random variation is also an essential feature of almost all working systems: a scientist taking measurements in a laboratory; an economist studying price fluctuations; a surgeon studying heartbeat patterns on an electrocardiogram; a disease spreading through a population. In all these processes, some elements of chance or randomness are present.

All the situations that are studied in M343 *Applications of probability* contain some element of chance. The approach taken is to describe a practical situation and then to develop a probability model that represents its main features. The model is then analysed mathematically in order to discover the possible ways in which the situation might develop and to calculate probabilities associated with them. The emphasis throughout is on modelling and problem-solving.

This book will provide you with a summary of the main ideas, techniques and results for probability and random variables that you will need as you work through *Books 2* to *5*, so it is important for you to study this book thoroughly now.

In Section 1, some fundamental ideas and results from probability theory are discussed. Several of the results will be used on many occasions.

Sections 2 to 5 are concerned with random variables. If you have studied a level 2 statistics module, then some of the material on discrete random variables in Section 2 will be familiar to you. Probability generating functions, which are used frequently from *Book 3* onwards, are introduced in Section 3. General techniques and results for continuous random variables are discussed in Section 4, and some specific standard distributions and their properties are described in Section 5.

On many occasions in M343, a model is developed for a random phenomenon, and the question arises as to whether the model is a reasonable one. One approach is to use simulation to obtain some idea of the sort of behaviour predicted by the model. The simulation of observations is discussed briefly in Section 6.

In Section 7, some of the ideas introduced in Sections 1 to 6 concerning relationships between two or more events or random variables are brought together and extended. Several of the results from this section are used in *Books 2* to *5*.

Section 8 contains a brief review of some of the mathematical results and techniques with which you are assumed to be familiar. Whether or not you work through any of this section is up to you: it is included for you to refer to if you are unsure of any of the material that it contains.

Section 9 consists of further exercises on the topics covered in Sections 1 to 6. These are there for you to try *if you need them*. Whether or not you attempt any of them is up to you.

1 Probability

Some knowledge of probability and its rules is essential in order to understand the development and analysis of models for random phenomena. A brief introduction to probability theory is given in this section. In Subsection 1.1, the language and notation of probability are discussed and some simple rules are obtained. The idea of conditional probability is introduced in Subsection 1.2, and some further rules are derived. An important result known as the Theorem of Total Probability is discussed in Subsection 1.3.

1.1 Basic ideas of probability

Many situations contain some element of chance: the toss of a coin may result in a head or a tail, the roll of a six-sided die may result in a score of 1, 2, 3, 4, 5 or 6, and so on. In each case, it is impossible to predict with certainty what the result will be.

The probability of an event is a number that quantifies the chance that the event will occur. It can be defined in a number of ways. For instance, the **probability of an event A**, which is denoted $P(A)$, may be defined to be the proportion of occasions in the long run on which the event A occurs. For example, if you were to toss a fair coin repeatedly, you would find that the proportion of tosses that result in a head approaches $\frac{1}{2}$ as the number of tosses becomes large. In the long run, half the tosses would result in a head, so the probability that a single toss results in a head is $\frac{1}{2}$.

Several properties of probabilities can be deduced from this definition. First, since the probability of an event A is a *proportion*, it must be a number between 0 and 1. An impossible event never occurs, so its probability is 0; and a certain event always occurs, so its probability is 1. These properties are summarised in the following box.

> **Properties of probabilities**
> ◇   For any event A, $0 \leq P(A) \leq 1$.
> ◇   If an event A is impossible, then $P(A) = 0$.
> ◇   If an event A is certain to happen, then $P(A) = 1$.

There are various rules for calculating probabilities. One rule concerns the **complement** $\overline{A}$ of an event A: $\overline{A}$ is the event 'not A', and $P(\overline{A})$ is the probability that A does not occur. Clearly, the proportion of the time that A does not happen is equal to 1 minus the proportion of the time that it does, so

$$P(\overline{A}) = 1 - P(A).$$

Another rule concerns the probability that one or other of two mutually exclusive events occurs: two events A and B are **mutually exclusive** if it is impossible for them to occur simultaneously, that is, if $P(A \cap B) = 0$. In this case, the proportion of the time that either A or B occurs is equal to the proportion of the time that A occurs plus the proportion of the time that B occurs. That is, for mutually exclusive events A and B,

$A \cap B$ is read 'A intersection B', and is mathematical shorthand for 'both A and B'.

$$P(A \cup B) = P(A) + P(B).$$

This rule can be extended to three or more mutually exclusive events. For instance, for mutually exclusive events A, B and C,

$A \cup B$ is read 'A union B', and is mathematical shorthand for 'A or B' (and in general covers 'A, or B, or both').

$$P(A \cup B \cup C) = P(A) + P(B) + P(C).$$

It would be cumbersome to argue in terms of long-run proportions every time you need to calculate a probability, and it would usually be impracticable to estimate probabilities by carrying out repeated experiments, so in practice, a more theoretical approach is needed. In this subsection, simple situations are considered in which an experiment or trial is performed and all the possible outcomes can be specified. It is certain that just one outcome will occur, but it is impossible to predict with certainty which one.

In many simple experiments, the outcomes can be assumed to be equally likely. If there are N possible equally likely outcomes of an experiment, then each has probability $1/N$. For example, when a fair coin is tossed, there are two equally likely outcomes, so the probability that it lands heads up is $\frac{1}{2}$, and the probability that it lands tails up is $\frac{1}{2}$: that is, $P(\text{head}) = P(\text{tail}) = \frac{1}{2}$.

Example 1.1 Rolling a die

When rolling a fair six-sided die, there are six equally likely outcomes, so the probability that it will land with a particular face uppermost is $\frac{1}{6}$, and in particular,

$$P(4) = \tfrac{1}{6}.$$

The probability that the score on the die will not be 4 is

$$P(\text{not } 4) = 1 - P(4) = 1 - \tfrac{1}{6} = \tfrac{5}{6}.$$

Since the six possible outcomes are mutually exclusive events, the probability of obtaining a score of either 3 or 4 is

$$P(3 \cup 4) = P(3) + P(4) = \tfrac{1}{6} + \tfrac{1}{6} = \tfrac{1}{3}.$$

And the probability that the score will be greater than 2 is

$$P(3 \cup 4 \cup 5 \cup 6) = P(3) + P(4) + P(5) + P(6) = \tfrac{1}{6} + \tfrac{1}{6} + \tfrac{1}{6} + \tfrac{1}{6} = \tfrac{2}{3}. \quad \blacklozenge$$

$P(3 \cup 4)$ means the probability $P(3 \text{ or } 4)$.

$P(3 \cup 4 \cup 5 \cup 6)$ means the probability $P(3 \text{ or } 4 \text{ or } 5 \text{ or } 6)$.

Activity 1.1 Rolling a die

Write down the probability of each of the following events associated with rolling a fair six-sided die.

(a) The score on the die is an even number.

(b) The score on the die is a number greater than 4.

(c) The score on the die is a number that is even and greater than 4.

(d) The score on the die is a number that is either even or greater than 4 (or both).

Example 1.2 The addition rule

Let A be the event that the score obtained when a fair six-sided die is rolled is an even number, and let B be the event that the score is a number greater than 4. In Activity 1.1, you found the probabilities $P(A)$, $P(B)$, $P(A \cap B)$ and $P(A \cup B)$ by counting equally likely outcomes. Of the six possible outcomes, three are even numbers, two are numbers greater than 4, one is a number that is both even and greater than 4, and four are either even or greater than 4 (or both). (This information is shown in the Venn diagram in Figure 1.1.) Therefore

$$P(A) = \tfrac{3}{6}, \quad P(B) = \tfrac{2}{6}, \quad P(A \cap B) = \tfrac{1}{6}, \quad P(A \cup B) = \tfrac{4}{6}.$$

Notice that in this example the events A and B are not mutually exclusive: A and B can occur simultaneously, so the probability $P(A \cup B)$ cannot be found simply by adding together the probabilities $P(A)$ and $P(B)$. As the diagram in Figure 1.1 shows, if you add together the number of outcomes in A and the

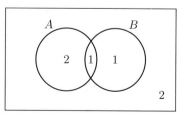

Figure 1.1 Numbers of equally likely outcomes

number of outcomes in B, then you count the number in $A \cap B$ twice. Thus to obtain the number of outcomes in $A \cup B$, the number in $A \cap B$ must be subtracted from the sum of the number in A and the number in B. Correspondingly, to find $P(A \cup B)$, $P(A \cap B)$ must be subtracted from $P(A) + P(B)$:

$$P(A \cup B) = P(A) + P(B) - P(A \cap B)$$
$$= \tfrac{3}{6} + \tfrac{2}{6} - \tfrac{1}{6}$$
$$= \tfrac{4}{6}. \quad \blacklozenge$$

Example 1.2 gives an illustration of the following rule, which is sometimes called the **addition rule**. For any two events A and B,

$$P(A \cup B) = P(A) + P(B) - P(A \cap B).$$

This rule specifies the probability of occurrence of at least one of *any* two events A and B. The rule holds whether or not A and B are mutually exclusive.

Three rules that are useful for calculating probabilities have now been discussed. They are summarised in the following box.

Rules of probability

◇ For any event A,

$$P(\overline{A}) = 1 - P(A). \tag{1.1}$$

◇ For mutually exclusive events A and B,

$$P(A \cup B) = P(A) + P(B). \tag{1.2}$$

◇ The **addition rule**: for any two events A and B,

$$P(A \cup B) = P(A) + P(B) - P(A \cap B). \tag{1.3}$$

Note that when A and B are mutually exclusive, $A \cap B = \varnothing$, so $P(A \cap B) = 0$ and hence (1.3) reduces to (1.2). Therefore (1.2) is just a special case of the addition rule (1.3).

The symbol $\varnothing$ represents the empty set.

Activity 1.2 Using the rules

Given $P(A) = 0.5$, $P(B) = 0.4$ and $P(A \cap B) = 0.1$, use rules (1.1) to (1.3) to calculate each of the following probabilities.

(a) $P(\overline{A})$ (b) $P(\overline{B})$ (c) $P(A \cup B)$ (d) $P(\overline{A} \cap \overline{B})$ (e) $P(A \cap \overline{B})$

You may find it helpful to draw Venn diagrams for parts (d) and (e).

M343 is about applying ideas and rules of probability to models for random phenomena. In any given situation, before any probabilities can be calculated, the events involved must be defined, as illustrated in Example 1.3.

Example 1.3 Weekend newspapers

On any weekend, the probability that Swarup buys a newspaper on Saturday is 0.45, and the probability that he buys a newspaper on Sunday is 0.75. The probability that he buys a newspaper on both days is 0.3. To calculate probabilities associated with this situation, the first step is to identify the events – that is, give them letters as names – and write down the given probabilities using these names. Then the rules can be used to calculate other probabilities.

Let A be the event that Swarup buys a newspaper on Saturday, and let B be the event that he buys a newspaper on Sunday. Then the probabilities can be written as

$$P(A) = 0.45, \quad P(B) = 0.75, \quad P(A \cap B) = 0.3.$$

What is the probability that Swarup buys a newspaper on at least one day during a particular weekend? What is the probability that he does not buy a newspaper on either Saturday or Sunday? And what is the probability that he buys a newspaper on Saturday but not on Sunday?

The probability that Swarup buys a newspaper on at least one day at the weekend is $P(A \cup B)$. Using (1.3) gives

$$P(A \cup B) = P(A) + P(B) - P(A \cap B)$$
$$= 0.45 + 0.75 - 0.3$$
$$= 0.9.$$

The probability that Swarup does not buy a newspaper on either Saturday or Sunday is $P(\overline{A} \cap \overline{B})$. Since $\overline{A} \cap \overline{B}$ is the complement of $A \cup B$, using (1.1) gives

$$P(\overline{A} \cap \overline{B}) = 1 - P(A \cup B) = 1 - 0.9 = 0.1.$$

For any events A and B,
$$\overline{A} \cap \overline{B} = \overline{A \cup B}.$$
(See the solution to Activity 1.2(d).)

The probability that Swarup buys a newspaper on Saturday but not on Sunday is $P(A \cap \overline{B})$. In part (e) of Activity 1.2, you saw that A must occur either with B or with $\overline{B}$, so

$$P(A \cap \overline{B}) = P(A) - P(A \cap B) = 0.45 - 0.3 = 0.15. \quad \blacklozenge$$

Activity 1.3   News bulletins

On any weekday, the probability that Swarup listens to the news at five o'clock is 0.45 and the probability that he listens to the news at six o'clock is 0.35. The probability that he does not listen to either news bulletin is 0.25.

(a) Identify the events involved by giving them names, and write down the given probabilities in terms of these names.

(b) Calculate the probability that Swarup listens to at least one of the news bulletins on any particular weekday.

(c) Calculate the probability that he listens to both news bulletins.

M343 is not concerned with the fine details involved in deriving the rules and techniques that are used. That would require a more mathematical approach to probability than has been adopted so far. This subsection ends with a brief description of one mathematical approach, which involves starting with a small set of rules, called the *axioms of probability*, and proving all subsequent rules assuming only these axioms. Probability might be introduced in the following way using this approach.

The set of all possible outcomes of an experiment, denoted Ω, is called the **event space**. For instance, if the experiment is rolling a six-sided die, then the event space is $\Omega = \{1, 2, 3, 4, 5, 6\}$.

An **event** A is defined as a subset of the event space Ω, so $A \subseteq \Omega$. An event may be a single outcome – for example, when a die is rolled, observing that the score is 6 – or it may contains several outcomes – for example, observing that the score is an even number.

Associated with every event A is a number $P(A)$ called the **probability of the (occurrence of the) event A**. A probability satisfies the three axioms given in the following box.

The words in parentheses are often omitted.

Axioms of probability

◇ $0 \leq P(A) \leq 1$ for every event A.

◇ $P(\Omega) = 1$.

◇   If $A_i \cap A_j = \varnothing$ for all i and j, then

$$P(A_1 \cup A_2 \cup \cdots \cup A_n) = \sum_{i=1}^{n} P(A_i).$$

The first axiom states that a probability is a number between 0 and 1 (inclusive). Since the event space Ω contains all possible outcomes, the second axiom expresses the fact that one or other of the outcomes must occur. The statement $A_i \cap A_j = \varnothing$ says that A_i and A_j are mutually exclusive events, and hence it is impossible for A_i and A_j to occur together. So the third axiom states that the probability that one or other of a set of mutually exclusive events will occur is equal to the sum of the separate probabilities of the events.

These axioms state properties that have been obtained in this section using a practical and intuitive approach to probability. They are stated in the *Handbook*, together with rules (1.1) to (1.3) and a number of other rules that are discussed in Subsections 1.2 and 1.3.

1.2 Conditional probability

The probability that an event occurs often depends on whether or not another event occurs. Consider, for instance, the scenario in Example 1.4.

Example 1.4   Rolling a die: dependent events

A fair six-sided die is rolled. Let A be the event that a score of 3 or less is obtained, and let E be the event that an even number is obtained; then $P(A) = \frac{1}{2}$ and $P(E) = \frac{1}{2}$.

Now suppose that it is known whether the score is an even number or an odd number – that is, it is known whether E or $\overline{E}$ has occurred. If it is known that the score is even (E), then there are three possible outcomes, one of which is a number less than or equal to 3, so in this case the probability that the score is 3 or less is $\frac{1}{3}$. On the other hand, if it is known that the score is odd ($\overline{E}$), then the probability that the score is 3 or less is $\frac{2}{3}$. Thus the probability that A occurs depends on whether or not E has occurred.   ◆

In general, the probability that an event A occurs when it is known that an event E has occurred is called the **conditional probability of A given E**, and is denoted by $P(A|E)$. It is defined as follows.

Conditional probability

The **conditional probability of A given E**, denoted $P(A|E)$, is the probability that an event A occurs when it is known that the event E has occurred. It is defined for any events A and E, provided that $P(E) \neq 0$, and is given by the formula

$$P(A|E) = \frac{P(A \cap E)}{P(E)}. \qquad (1.4)$$

Example 1.5   Rolling a die: conditional probabilities

When a die is rolled, only one of the six possible outcomes of rolling the die is both even (event E) and less than or equal to 3 (event A) – namely 2 – so $P(A \cap E) = \frac{1}{6}$. Also, $P(E) = \frac{1}{2}$. The formula in the definition of conditional probability (1.4) gives

Events A and E were defined in Example 1.4.

$$P(A|E) = \frac{P(A \cap E)}{P(E)} = \frac{\frac{1}{6}}{\frac{1}{2}} = \frac{1}{3}.$$

This confirms the result obtained in Example 1.4 by counting outcomes.   ◆

Activity 1.4   Conditional probabilities

For the events A and B of Activity 1.2, use (1.4) to find the value of each of the following conditional probabilities.

(a) $P(A|B)$ (b) $P(A|\overline{B})$ (c) $P(\overline{A}|\overline{B})$ (d) $P(B|A)$

In the solution to Activity 1.4, $P(A|\overline{B})$ and $P(\overline{A}|\overline{B})$ were found by applying the definition of conditional probability. Alternatively, after finding $P(A|\overline{B})$, $P(\overline{A}|\overline{B})$ could have been found by noting that given $\overline{B}$ occurs, either A or $\overline{A}$ must occur, so

$$P(A|\overline{B}) + P(\overline{A}|\overline{B}) = 1.$$

This is an example of the following general result: for any events A and E (with $P(E) \neq 0$),

$$P(A|E) + P(\overline{A}|E) = 1.$$

Activity 1.5   News bulletins: conditional probabilities

In the solution to Activity 1.3, the events A and B were defined: A is the event that Swarup listens to the news at five o'clock, and B is the event that he listens to the news at six o'clock.

(a) Given that Swarup listened to the news at five o'clock one day, calculate the probability that he also listened to the news at six o'clock.

(b) Given that he did not listen to the news at five o'clock, calculate the probability that he did not listen to the news at six o'clock.

(c) If it is known that he listened to the news at six o'clock, what is the probability that he also listened to the news at five o'clock?

(d) If it is known that he listened to the news at six o'clock, what is the probability that he did not listen to the news at five o'clock?

Formula (1.4), which defines the conditional probability $P(A|E)$, can be rearranged to give a formula for the joint probability $P(A \cap E)$ in terms of $P(E)$ and the conditional probability $P(A|E)$:

$$P(A \cap E) = P(A|E)\, P(E). \tag{1.5}$$

You will find this form useful in Activity 1.6.

Activity 1.6   Rainfall

Suppose that the probability of rainfall tomorrow depends on today's weather. If it rains today, then the probability that it will rain tomorrow is 0.7; while if today is dry, then the probability that it will rain tomorrow is 0.55. Suppose further that the probability that it will rain today is 0.6. Let R be the event that it will rain today, and let S be the event that it will rain tomorrow.

(a) Write down all the probabilities given above using the event names R and S.

(b) Calculate the probability that it will rain both today and tomorrow.

(c) Calculate the probability that it will rain neither today nor tomorrow.

Formula (1.5), which follows from the definition of conditional probability, can be used to obtain an important result that will be used on many occasions in M343.

For any two events A and B,

$$P(A \cap B) = P(A|B)\,P(B)$$

and

$$P(B \cap A) = P(B|A)\,P(A).$$

Since $P(A \cap B) = P(B \cap A)$, it follows that

$$P(A|B)\,P(B) = P(B|A)\,P(A).$$

Dividing by $P(B)$ leads to the following result, which is known as **Bayes' formula**.

Bayes' formula

For any two events A and B,

$$P(A|B) = \frac{P(B|A)\,P(A)}{P(B)}, \quad \text{provided } P(B) \neq 0. \tag{1.6}$$

Example 1.6   Daily newspapers

Suppose that 40% of a newsagent's regular customers buy a morning newspaper every day, while 25% buy an evening newspaper daily. Of those customers who buy a morning newspaper every day, 55% also buy an evening newspaper daily.

One customer, Tom, is selected at random from the regular customers. If it is known that Tom buys an evening newspaper daily, what is the probability that he also buys a morning newspaper every day?

To answer this question, the events involved must first be defined. Let M be the event that Tom buys a morning newspaper every day, and let E be the event that he buys an evening newspaper every day. The probabilities may be written as

$$P(M) = 0.4, \quad P(E) = 0.25, \quad P(E|M) = 0.55.$$

The probability required is $P(M|E)$. Using Bayes' formula,

$$P(M|E) = \frac{P(E|M)\,P(M)}{P(E)} = \frac{0.55 \times 0.4}{0.25} = 0.88.$$

So the probability that Tom also buys a morning newspaper every day is 0.88.

Now suppose that Tom does not buy an evening newspaper daily. In this case, what is the probability that he buys a morning newspaper every day, and what is the probability that he does not buy a morning newspaper every day?

In this case, the probability that Tom buys a morning newspaper every day is $P(M|\overline{E})$. Using Bayes' formula,

$$P(M|\overline{E}) = \frac{P(\overline{E}|M)\,P(M)}{P(\overline{E})}.$$

Since $P(\overline{E}|M) = 1 - P(E|M)$ and $P(\overline{E}) = 1 - P(E)$,

$$P(M|\overline{E}) = \frac{(1 - 0.55) \times 0.4}{1 - 0.25} = 0.24.$$

So, given the information that Tom does not buy an evening newspaper every day, the probability that he buys a morning newspaper every day is 0.24. It follows that the probability that he does not buy a morning newspaper every day is

$$P(\overline{M}|\overline{E}) = 1 - P(M|\overline{E}) = 0.76. \quad \blacklozenge$$

Activity 1.7   Solving problems

Suppose that a group of children is given two problems to solve, the second of which is more difficult than the first. Two-thirds of the children solve the first problem correctly, and three-fifths of them solve the second correctly. However, if a child solves the first problem correctly, then he or she has a conditional probability of $\frac{3}{4}$ of also solving the second problem correctly.

One child, Anna, is selected at random from the group. Let F be the event that Anna solves the first problem correctly, and let S be the event that she solves the second problem correctly.

(a) Write down all the probabilities given above using the event names F and S.

(b) If it is known that Anna solved the second problem correctly, calculate the probability that she also solved the first problem correctly.

(c) It is known that Anna did not solve the first problem correctly. Calculate the conditional probability that she solved the second problem correctly. Also calculate the conditional probability that she did not solve the second problem correctly.

If the occurrence of an event A does not depend on whether or not another event E has occurred, then the events A and E are said to be **independent**. In this case, $P(A|E) = P(A)$, and formula (1.5) for $P(A \cap E)$ reduces to

$$P(A \cap E) = P(A)\,P(E).$$

This formula can be used to define the independence of two events as follows.

> **Independent events**
>
> The events A and E are said to be independent if
>
> $$P(A \cap E) = P(A)\,P(E). \tag{1.7}$$

Activity 1.8 Independent defects

The probability that a manufactured article has a defect of a certain type is 0.1, and the probability that it has a defect of another type is 0.05. The two types of defect occur independently.

An article is chosen at random. Let A be the event that the article has a defect of the first type, and let B be the event that it has a defect of the second type.

(a) Calculate the probability that the article has both types of defect.

(b) Calculate the probability that the article has exactly one of the two types of defect.

1.3 The Theorem of Total Probability

In this subsection, another result that will be used on many occasions is introduced. This result depends on the idea of a set of mutually exclusive and exhaustive events, as described below.

The events $E_1, E_2, \ldots, E_n$ are said to be **mutually exclusive and exhaustive** if only one of the events can occur at a time and if one or other of them must occur. That is,

$$E_i \cap E_j = \varnothing \quad \text{for } i \neq j, \ 1 \le i, j \le n,$$

and

$$E_1 \cup E_2 \cup \cdots \cup E_n = \Omega.$$

(This is illustrated in the Venn diagram in Figure 1.2 for $n = 4$.)

If the events $E_1, E_2, \ldots, E_n$ are mutually exclusive and exhaustive, and A is another event, then A must occur with one of the events $E_1, E_2, \ldots, E_n$, so

$$A = (A \cap E_1) \cup (A \cap E_2) \cup \cdots \cup (A \cap E_n).$$

(This is illustrated in Figure 1.3 for a set of four mutually exclusive and exhaustive events.)

The events $A \cap E_1, A \cap E_2, \ldots, A \cap E_n$ are mutually exclusive so, using (1.2),

$$P(A) = P(A \cap E_1) + P(A \cap E_2) + \cdots + P(A \cap E_n).$$

Then using (1.5) gives

$$P(A) = P(A|E_1)\,P(E_1) + P(A|E_2)\,P(E_2) + \cdots + P(A|E_n)\,P(E_n).$$

This result gives an expression for the probability of occurrence of an event A when A occurs simultaneously with one of a set of mutually exclusive and exhaustive events $E_1, E_2, \ldots, E_n$. It is known as the **Theorem of Total Probability**, and is stated formally in the following box.

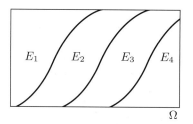

Figure 1.2 A set of four mutually exclusive and exhaustive events

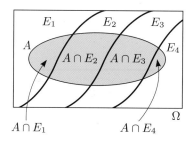

Figure 1.3 A must occur with one of E_1, E_2, E_3 and E_4

The Theorem of Total Probability

For any event A,

$$P(A) = \sum_{i=1}^{n} P(A|E_i)\,P(E_i), \tag{1.8}$$

where $E_1, E_2, \ldots, E_n$ are mutually exclusive and exhaustive events.

A special case of this result is obtained by observing that E and $\overline{E}$ are mutually exclusive and exhaustive events: for any two events A and E,

$$P(A) = P(A|E)\,P(E) + P(A|\overline{E})\,P(\overline{E}). \tag{1.9}$$

Example 1.7   Does Sam's car start first time?

Whether or not Sam can start his car first time in the morning depends on whether or not he put it in the garage the evening before. If he did, then the probability that the car starts first time is 0.8. If he did not, then the probability that the car starts first time is only 0.15. The probability that he puts his car in the garage is 0.9. In the long run, on what proportion of mornings does Sam's car start first time?

Let F be the event that the car starts first time, and let G be the event that the car was put in the garage the previous evening. Then

$$P(F|G) = 0.8, \quad P(F|\overline{G}) = 0.15, \quad P(G) = 0.9.$$

The proportion required is given by the probability $P(F)$.

By the Theorem of Total Probability (in the form (1.9)),

$$P(F) = P(F|G)\,P(G) + P(F|\overline{G})\,P(\overline{G})$$
$$= 0.8 \times 0.9 + 0.15 \times (1 - 0.9)$$
$$= 0.735.$$

Therefore Sam's car starts first time on 73.5% of mornings in the long run. ◆

Activities 1.9 and 1.10 will give you some practice at applying the Theorem of Total Probability and some of the other results discussed in this section.

Activity 1.9   Screening tests

A diagnostic screening test for a particular disease has been shown empirically to be fairly reliable: a positive result is recorded in 96% of cases where a patient actually has the disease, and in 3% of cases where the patient is healthy. The disease is known to afflict 1 person in 250. Let R be the event that a positive result is recorded, and let D be the event that a patient has the disease.

(a) Write down the given information as probabilities involving the events R and D.

(b) Calculate the probability that a patient will screen positive on this diagnostic test.

(c) Calculate the probability that a person who screens positive is actually suffering from the disease.

Activity 1.10   Verdicts

A judicial court in a certain country may return any one of the three verdicts 'guilty', 'not guilty' and 'not proven'. Of the cases tried by this court, 70% of the verdicts are 'guilty', 20% are 'not guilty', and 10% are 'not proven'. Suppose that when the court's verdict is 'guilty' the probability that the accused is actually innocent is 0.05, and that the corresponding probabilities when the verdicts are 'not guilty' and 'not proven' are 0.95 and 0.25, respectively. Let G, N and U be the events that the verdicts 'guilty', 'not guilty' and 'not proven' are returned, respectively. Let I be the event that an accused person is innocent.

(a) Write down the given information as probabilities involving the events G, N, U and I.

(b) Calculate the probability that an accused person is actually innocent.

(c) Calculate the probability that an innocent person will be found 'guilty'.

Summary of Section 1

In this section, some of the language and notation of probability has been introduced. Some basic properties of probabilities have been discussed, and several rules for calculating probabilities have been given. Conditional probability has been defined, and Bayes' formula and the Theorem of Total Probability have been introduced. The results described in this section will be used on many occasions in *Books 2* to *5*.

Exercises on Section 1

Exercise 1.1   Practice at using the rules

Given $P(A) = 0.3$, $P(B) = 0.6$ and $P(A \cap B) = 0.2$, find the value of each of the following probabilities.

(a) $P(\overline{A})$ (b) $P(\overline{B})$ (c) $P(A \cup B)$ (d) $P(\overline{A} \cap \overline{B})$ (e) $P(\overline{A} \cap B)$

Exercise 1.2   Further practice

Given $P(B) = 0.4$, $P(A|B) = 0.65$ and $P(A|\overline{B}) = 0.35$, find the values of the following probabilities.

(a) $P(A \cap B)$ (b) $P(A)$ (c) $P(A \cup B)$

Exercise 1.3   Yet more practice

Given $P(A) = 0.5$, $P(B|A) = 0.4$ and $P(A \cup B) = 0.9$, find the values of the following probabilities.

(a) $P(A \cap B)$ (b) $P(B)$ (c) $P(A|B)$

Exercise 1.4   Defective articles

Machine 1 and machine 2 produce 60% and 40%, respectively, of the total daily output of a factory. It is known that 2% of items produced on machine 1 and 5% of items produced on machine 2 are defective.

One item is chosen at random from a day's production.

(a) Identify the events involved by giving them names, and write down the given information as probabilities involving these events.

(b) Calculate the probability that the chosen item is defective.

(c) Given that the chosen item is defective, calculate the probability that it was produced on machine 1.

2   Discrete random variables

This section contains a summary of results and techniques concerning discrete random variables. In Subsection 2.1, a random variable is defined and the probability mass function of a discrete random variable is introduced. The independence of random variables is also discussed briefly. The main properties of six families of discrete distributions are summarised in Subsection 2.2. Expectation for discrete random variables is discussed in Subsections 2.3 and 2.4.

2.1   Random variables

Chance is a feature of many situations. For instance, if light bulbs are tested to failure, then the time until a bulb fails varies from bulb to bulb. So the time until a randomly chosen bulb fails is a random quantity: it is an example of a **random variable** or **variate**. Other examples include the height of a randomly chosen woman, the number of children in a randomly chosen household, and the number of calls to a telephone helpline in a two-hour period.

'Variate' and 'random variable' are synonyms. Both terms are used frequently throughout M343.

The set of all the possible values that a random variable can take is called its **range**. When the range contains only a finite or countably infinite number of values, the random variable is said to be **discrete**. The random variables N, the number of children in a household, and C, the number of calls to a helpline, are discrete random variables. On the other hand, each of the other two random variables above – T, the time to failure of a bulb, and H, the height of a woman – can take any value in an interval of values; they are examples of **continuous** random variables. Continuous random variables are discussed in Section 4. This section is devoted to discrete random variables.

Example 2.1   The score on a die

A simple example will be used to illustrate the main ideas concerning discrete random variables. Let X be the score obtained when a fair die is rolled; then the range of X is $\{1, 2, 3, 4, 5, 6\}$. The **probability mass function**, or **p.m.f.**, of X specifies the probability that X takes each value x in the range. The p.m.f. of X is denoted $p_X(x)$, so for each x in the range of X,

$$p_X(x) = P(X = x).$$

For the score on a die,

$$p_X(x) = \tfrac{1}{6}, \quad x = 1, 2, \ldots, 6.$$

The subscript X is usually omitted unless there is any ambiguity. Thus the p.m.f. of the score on a die would usually be written simply as

$$p(x) = \tfrac{1}{6}, \quad x = 1, 2, \ldots, 6. \quad \blacklozenge$$

Activity 2.1   Another random variable

In a game, a fair six-sided die is rolled. If the score on the die is 6, then a player moves three spaces forward; if it is 4 or 5, then he moves two spaces forward; and if it is 1, 2 or 3, then he moves one space backward. Let Y represent the number of spaces that the player moves forward when the die is rolled.

(a) What is the range of the random variable Y?

(b) Write down the p.m.f. of Y.

Example 2.1 and Activity 2.1 illustrate the fact that there can be more than one random variable associated with an experiment. In a practical situation, the choice of random variable is governed by the problem to be solved.

In Section 1, you saw how the development of a mathematical theory of probability might begin. In such a theory, a mathematical definition of a random variable is required in place of the informal description just given. Formally, if Ω is the event space of an experiment, then a **random variable** is defined to be a function with domain Ω and codomain $\mathbb{R}$. The image set of a random variable X is called its **range** and is denoted Ω_X.

The notation Ω_X for the range of a random variable X is a useful shorthand. For instance, using this notation, the basic properties of a p.m.f. can be written in a concise form as in the following box.

Properties of probability mass functions

For a discrete random variable X with p.m.f. $p_X(x)$ and range Ω_X:

◇ $0 < p_X(x) \leq 1$ for all $x \in \Omega_X$;

◇ $\displaystyle\sum_{x \in \Omega_X} p_X(x) = 1.$

The first property follows from the fact that for each x in the range of X, $p_X(x)$ is a probability and hence its value lies between 0 and 1. The second property follows because the value of X must be one of the values in the range, so the sum of all the probabilities $p_X(x)$ must be equal to 1.

Independent random variables

The idea of independence was introduced for events in Subsection 1.2: two events A and E are said to be independent if the occurrence of one event does not depend on whether or not the other event has occurred, and if this is the case then

$$P(A \cap E) = P(A)\,P(E).$$

In a similar way, two random variables X and Y are said to be **independent** if the occurrence of any event associated with X does not depend on the occurrence of any event associated with Y. For discrete random variables this is equivalent to the following condition:

$$P(X = x, Y = y) = P(X = x)\,P(Y = y) \quad \text{for all } x \in \Omega_X,\ y \in \Omega_Y.$$

The joint probability $P(X = x, Y = y)$ is denoted $p(x, y)$, so this condition may be written

$$p(x, y) = p_X(x)\,p_Y(y) \quad \text{for all } x \in \Omega_X,\ y \in \Omega_Y.$$

The comma in the probability $P(X = x, Y = y)$ may be read as 'and'.

Example 2.2   *Rolling two dice: independent random variables*

Suppose that a red die and a blue die are rolled. If X is the score on the red die and Y is the score on the blue die then, since there are 36 equally likely possible outcomes for the pair of scores,

$$p(x, y) = \tfrac{1}{36}, \quad x = 1, 2, \ldots, 6,\ y = 1, 2, \ldots, 6.$$

There are six equally likely possible outcomes for the score on a single die, so

$$p_X(x) = \tfrac{1}{6}, \quad x = 1, 2, \ldots, 6,$$
$$p_Y(y) = \tfrac{1}{6}, \quad y = 1, 2, \ldots, 6.$$

Therefore

$$p(x, y) = p_X(x)\,p_Y(y), \quad x = 1, 2, \ldots, 6,\ y = 1, 2, \ldots, 6.$$

Hence the random variables X and Y are independent.   ◆

Example 2.3   Rolling a die: dependent random variables

Suppose that X is the score obtained when a die is rolled, and that Y is a random variable that takes the value 1 if the score is even and the value 0 if the score is odd. Then, for example,

$$p(2,1) = P(X = 2, Y = 1) = \tfrac{1}{6}.$$

But

$$p_X(2) = \tfrac{1}{6} \quad \text{and} \quad p_Y(1) = \tfrac{1}{2},$$

so

$$p_X(2)\,p_Y(1) = \tfrac{1}{6} \times \tfrac{1}{2} = \tfrac{1}{12}.$$

Therefore

$$p(2,1) \neq p_X(2)\,p_Y(1).$$

Hence in this case the random variables X and Y are not independent.   ◆

The independence of discrete random variables is discussed further in Subsection 7.1.

2.2   Specific probability distributions

There are several standard families of discrete distributions that occur repeatedly in probability models of real-life situations. In this subsection they are listed, together with their p.m.f.s, and examples of situations to which they are appropriate are given.

The discrete uniform distribution

The random variable X is said to have a **discrete uniform distribution**, or to be uniformly distributed, if

$$p(x) = \frac{1}{n}, \quad x = 1, 2, \ldots, n.$$

The score obtained when a fair six-sided die is rolled can be modelled by a discrete uniform distribution with $n = 6$.

The Bernoulli distribution

A **Bernoulli trial** is an experiment that has precisely two outcomes: either an event E occurs or it does not. These outcomes are often described as 'success' or 'failure', and their probabilities are denoted by p and $q(= 1 - p)$, respectively. A random variable X is said to have a **Bernoulli distribution** with parameter p if $P(X = 1) = p$ and $P(X = 0) = q$. The p.m.f. of X can be written

$$p(x) = p^x q^{1-x}, \quad x = 0, 1.$$

$a^0 = 1$ for all $a \geq 0$.

The binomial distribution

Suppose that a sequence of n independent Bernoulli trials is performed. At each trial either a success occurs, with probability p, or a failure occurs, with probability $1 - p = q$. The total number of successes in n trials is a random variable Y with range $\{0, 1, \ldots, n\}$. The p.m.f. of Y is given by

$$p(y) = \binom{n}{y} p^y q^{n-y}, \quad y = 0, 1, \ldots, n, \tag{2.1}$$

where

$$\binom{n}{y} = \frac{n!}{y!\,(n-y)!} \quad (y! = 1 \times 2 \times \cdots \times y).$$

$0!$ is defined to be 1.

The random variable Y is said to have a **binomial distribution** with parameters n and p, and this is written $Y \sim B(n, p)$.

If X_i is the Bernoulli variate representing the result of the ith trial, then $X_i \sim B(1,p)$. Since $X_i = 1$ if and only if the ith trial results in success, it follows that

$$Y = X_1 + X_2 + \cdots + X_n.$$

Therefore the binomial variate Y is equal to the sum of n independent Bernoulli variates.

A common source of error when calculating binomial probabilities is in the evaluation of the binomial coefficients $\binom{n}{y}$. Activity 2.2 will give you some practice at evaluating them. If your calculator gives binomial coefficients, then check your answers using your calculator.

Activity 2.2   Calculating binomial coefficients

Find the values of the following binomial coefficients.

(a) $\binom{5}{2}$ (b) $\binom{8}{6}$ (c) $\binom{10}{7}$ (d) $\binom{9}{1}$ (e) $\binom{6}{3}$ (f) $\binom{7}{0}$

Example 2.4   Arriving late

Suppose that Jim is late for work a third of the time, and that whether he is late on any particular day is independent of whether he is late on any other day. Then Y, the number of days on which he is late in a five-day working week, has a binomial distribution: $Y \sim B(5, \frac{1}{3})$. The probability that he is late twice in a particular week is given by

$$P(Y = 2) = \binom{5}{2} \left(\tfrac{1}{3}\right)^2 \left(\tfrac{2}{3}\right)^3$$

$$= \frac{5!}{2!\,3!} \times \frac{1}{9} \times \frac{8}{27}$$

$$= 10 \times \frac{8}{243} = \frac{80}{243} \simeq 0.3292. \quad \blacklozenge$$

Activity 2.3   Calculating binomial probabilities

Calculate the following probabilities.

(a) $P(Y = 4)$, where $Y \sim B(7, 0.3)$

(b) $P(V = 3)$, where $V \sim B(10, 0.6)$

(c) $P(W = 10)$, where $W \sim B(14, 0.42)$

(d) $P(Z \leq 2)$, where $Z \sim B(6, \frac{1}{2})$

The geometric distribution

In many situations, the same physical process can be studied from different points of view, giving rise to different random variables. The random variable Y that represents the total number of successes in n Bernoulli trials, has the binomial distribution $B(n, p)$. Another random variable associated with a sequence of Bernoulli trials is X, the number of trials up to and including the first success.

The random variable X has a **geometric distribution** with parameter p, written $X \sim G_1(p)$. The range of X is $\{1, 2, \ldots\}$, so for this distribution the range is infinite. The event $[X = x]$ occurs if the first $x - 1$ trials result in failure and then the xth trial results in a success. Hence the p.m.f. of X is

Square brackets are sometimes used to denote an event.

$$p(x) = q^{x-1}p, \quad x = 1, 2, \ldots.$$

As usual, in the context of Bernoulli trials, $q = 1 - p$.

An event associated with this distribution that is sometimes of interest is $[X \geq k]$, the event that at least k trials are required to achieve a success. The probability of this event can be calculated directly by summation:

$$P(X \geq k) = \sum_{x=k}^{\infty} p(x)$$
$$= q^{k-1}p + q^k p + q^{k+1}p + \cdots$$
$$= q^{k-1}p(1 + q + q^2 + \cdots)$$
$$= \frac{q^{k-1}p}{1 - q}$$
$$= q^{k-1} \quad (\text{since } 1 - q = p).$$

For $|x| < 1$,

$$1 + x + x^2 + \cdots = \frac{1}{1 - x}.$$

Alternatively, this probability can be calculated by noting that the event $[X \geq k]$ is equivalent to the event that the first $k - 1$ trials all result in failure. Since each trial results in a failure with probability q, the probability that the first $k - 1$ trials all result in failure is q^{k-1}. Hence if $X \sim G_1(p)$, then

$$P(X \geq k) = q^{k-1}. \tag{2.2}$$

This result is in the *Handbook*.

Activity 2.4   Hitting the bull's-eye

Robert is a keen archer. From a certain distance, the probability that he hits the bull's-eye with each shot is 0.3.

(a) Calculate the probability that Robert requires exactly three shots to hit the bull's-eye.

(b) Calculate the probability that he requires more than five shots to hit the bull's-eye.

There are two families of geometric distributions. One consists of random variables with range $\{1, 2, \ldots\}$ that are used to model the number of trials up to and including the first success in a sequence of Bernoulli trials. This family has just been described. The second family consists of random variables with range $\{0, 1, \ldots\}$ that can be used to model the number of successes before the first failure.

Consider the random variable Z, the number of successful trials *before* failure occurs (but not including the trial at which the failure occurs). For example, a trial could be the use of a piece of machinery and Z would represent the number of times it is used before breakdown. The smallest value of Z is 0, corresponding to the machine being broken down before its first attempted use (in this case, there are no successes before the first failure). The range of Z is $\Omega_Z = \{0, 1, \ldots\}$, and the p.m.f. of Z is

$$p(z) = qp^z, \quad z = 0, 1, \ldots.$$

This is written $Z \sim G_0(p)$.

Activity 2.5   *Mistakes at a cashpoint*

The probability that Sarah goes through the procedures to withdraw money at a cashpoint correctly is 0.8. Whether or not she makes a mistake at an attempt to withdraw money is independent of whether she makes a mistake at any other attempt.

Calculate the probability that Sarah makes fewer than five withdrawals before making a mistake.

Notice that different notations are used for the two families of geometric distributions: $G_0(p)$ is used when the range is $\{0, 1, \ldots\}$, and $G_1(p)$ when the range is $\{1, 2, \ldots\}$. These notations are useful as they provide a clear and concise way of specifying which geometric distribution is being used in any given situation.

The negative binomial distribution

The negative binomial distribution is a generalisation of the geometric distribution. If X is the number of Bernoulli trials up to and including the kth success, then X has a **negative binomial distribution** with parameters k and p. The number of trials must be at least k, so for this distribution the range is $\{k, k+1, \ldots\}$. The p.m.f. is derived by noting that if the random variable X takes the value x, then in the first $x - 1$ trials, there must have been $k - 1$ successes and hence $x - k$ failures. Then a success must occur at the xth trial. Thus the probability of occurrence of the event $[X = x]$ is given by the binomial probability (2.1) with $n = x - 1$ and $y = k - 1$, multiplied by p. Hence the p.m.f. of the negative binomial distribution is

$$p(x) = \binom{x-1}{k-1} p^k q^{x-k}, \quad x = k, k+1, \ldots.$$

Activity 2.6   *Hitting the bull's-eye*

If Robert shoots arrows at the target until he has hit the bull's-eye three times (see Activity 2.4), calculate the probability that he shoots exactly seven arrows.

As for the geometric distribution, the negative binomial distribution sometimes occurs with range $\{0, 1, \ldots\}$. In this case, it is the distribution of the number of successes occurring in a sequence of Bernoulli trials before the kth failure. Both families of negative binomial distributions are included in the table of discrete probability distributions in the *Handbook*, so you can look up the formulas for their p.m.f.s whenever you need them.

Note that when specifying either a geometric distribution or a negative binomial distribution, it is essential to give the range as well as the value(s) of the parameter(s) in order to avoid ambiguity.

The Poisson distribution

The random variable Z has a **Poisson distribution** with parameter μ if its p.m.f. is

The symbol μ is pronounced 'mew'.

$$p(z) = \frac{e^{-\mu}\mu^z}{z!}, \quad z = 0, 1, \ldots.$$

This is written $Z \sim \text{Poisson}(\mu)$. The Poisson distribution is closely linked with the Poisson process, which is discussed in *Book 2*. It provides a satisfactory model for such diverse situations as the numbers of misprints on a page, goals in a football match, white corpuscles in a small sample of blood, and eggs laid by a bird. Activity 2.7 will give you some practice at calculating Poisson probabilities.

Activity 2.7   Misprints

The number of misprints on a page in a book may be modelled by a Poisson distribution with parameter 2.5.

(a) Calculate the probability that a page contains no misprints.

(b) Calculate the probability that a page contains more than three misprints.

A binomial distribution with parameters n and p can be approximated by a Poisson distribution with parameter $\mu = np$ when n is large and p is small. Thus the Poisson distribution provides a model that can be used in situations that involve a large number of Bernoulli trials with a very small probability of success. This result, which is known as **Poisson's approximation for rare events**, is stated formally in the following box.

Poisson's approximation for rare events

For large values of n and small values of p, the binomial distribution $B(n, p)$ is approximately the same as the Poisson distribution with parameter np:

$$B(n, p) \approx \text{Poisson}(np).$$

The symbol '$\approx$' is read as 'is approximately the same distribution as'.

The approximation improves as n increases.

A rough rule

If n is large and p is small ($n \geq 50$ and $p \leq 0.05$, say), the approximation is good. The smallest value of n for which the approximation is good decreases as the value of p decreases.

Activity 2.8   A blood condition

The probability that a man has a certain blood condition is 0.04.

(a) Write down the exact distribution of the number of men who have the blood condition in a group of 100.

(b) Calculate an approximate value for the probability that in a group of 100 men, fewer than three have the blood condition.

Activity 2.9 will give you some practice at choosing an appropriate probability distribution.

Activity 2.9   Choosing a probability model

The probability that a randomly selected car is white is 0.2. State the distribution of each of the following random variables. You should include the values of any parameters (and, in the case of the geometric and negative binomial distributions, the range).

(a) X, where $X = 1$ if the next car that passes an observer is white and $X = 0$ otherwise.

(b) Y, the number of cars that pass an observer up to and including the first white one.

(c) W, the number of cars that are not white in a car park containing 50 cars.

(d) V, the number of white cars that pass an observer before the third non-white one.

2.3   The mean of a discrete random variable

The **mean** of a discrete random variable X (or of the probability distribution of X) is denoted by the Greek lower-case letter μ, and is given by

$$\mu = \sum_{x \in \Omega_X} x\, p(x).$$

That is, the mean is calculated by finding the sum of the products $x\, p(x)$, where the sum is taken over the range of X.

The mean of a random variable X is also called the **expected value** of X, or the **expectation** of X, and correspondingly denoted by $E(X)$. The different terminologies and notation for the mean of a discrete random variable are summarised in the following box.

> **The mean of a discrete random variable**
>
> For a discrete random variable X with p.m.f. $p(x)$, the **mean** of X, or **expected value** of X, or **expectation** of X, is given by
>
> $$\mu = E(X) = \sum_{x \in \Omega_X} x\, p(x). \tag{2.3}$$

Example 2.5   The mean of a Bernoulli distribution

The expected value of a Bernoulli variate $X \sim B(1, p)$ is

$$\mu = E(X) = 0 \times q + 1 \times p = p. \quad \blacklozenge$$

Activity 2.10   Calculating the mean

Find the expected value of the random variable X that has the p.m.f. in Table 2.1.

Table 2.1   The p.m.f. of X

x	1	2	3	4
$p(x)$	0.4	0.3	0.2	0.1

In Example 2.5 and Activity 2.10, the calculation involved in finding the mean was straightforward. However, this is not always so. There is an alternative formula for the mean that occasionally simplifies the calculation. The formula is derived below, so that you can see how it arises. You will not be expected to reproduce the derivation, just to apply the result.

The alternative formula for the mean contains the **cumulative distribution function** of X, denoted $F(x)$, which is defined as

$$F(x) = P(X \leq x), \quad x \in \mathbb{R}.$$

The cumulative distribution function (c.d.f.) is defined for all $x \in \mathbb{R}$. When X is a discrete variate, it is a step function with jumps at each point in the range and no others.

The alternative formula for the mean applies only when the range Ω_X is a subset of $\{0, 1, \ldots\}$, that is, when the only possible values x of X are non-negative integers, so that $P(X \geq 0) = 1$. In this case, for each $x \in \Omega_X$,

$$F(x) = P(X \leq x) = p(0) + p(1) + \cdots + p(x).$$

In order to derive the alternative formula for the mean, it is convenient to introduce the function Q defined by

$$Q(x) = 1 - F(x), \quad x \in \Omega_X.$$

Then

$$\begin{aligned} Q(x) &= 1 - P(X \leq x) \\ &= P(X > x) \\ &= \sum_{i=x+1}^{\infty} p(i). \end{aligned}$$

From (2.3),

$$\mu = E(X) = \sum_{x=0}^{\infty} x\, p(x).$$

That is,

$$\begin{aligned} \mu = E(X) &= p(1) + 2\,p(2) + 3\,p(3) + \cdots \\ &= p(1) + p(2) + p(3) + \cdots \\ &\quad\quad + p(2) + p(3) + \cdots \\ &\quad\quad\quad\quad + p(3) + \cdots \\ &\quad\quad\quad\quad\quad \vdots \\ &= Q(0) + Q(1) + Q(2) + \cdots \\ &= \sum_{x=0}^{\infty} Q(x) \\ &= \sum_{x=0}^{\infty} (1 - F(x)). \end{aligned}$$

This result is summarised in the following box.

An alternative formula for the mean

The mean of a non-negative discrete random variable X with c.d.f. $F(x)$ is given by

$$\mu = E(X) = \sum_{x=0}^{\infty} (1 - F(x)). \tag{2.4}$$

Example 2.6   Using the alternative formula for the mean

Values of the c.d.f. of the random variable X of Activity 2.10 are given in Table 2.2.

Table 2.2   Values of the c.d.f.

x	0	1	2	3	4	5	$\cdots$
$p(x)$	0	0.4	0.3	0.2	0.1	0	$\cdots$
$F(x)$	0	0.4	0.7	0.9	1	1	$\cdots$

Using the alternative formula for the mean (2.4) gives

$$\mu = E(X) = \sum_{x=0}^{\infty}(1 - F(x))$$
$$= (1 - F(0)) + (1 - F(1)) + (1 - F(2)) + \cdots$$
$$= 1 + 0.6 + 0.3 + 0.1 + 0 + 0 + \cdots$$
$$= 2.$$

Note that the sum includes a term for $x = 0$ even though $F(0) = 0$.

This value is the same as that obtained in Activity 2.10 using (2.3).   ◆

Activity 2.11   Using the alternative formula

The probability mass function of a random variable X is given in Table 2.3.

(a) Calculate the value of the c.d.f. of X for each of the values 0, 1, 2, 3, 4, and display these values in a table.

(b) Use the alternative formula (2.4) for the mean to find the expected value of X.

Table 2.3   The p.m.f. of X

x	2	3	4
$p(x)$	0.3	0.5	0.2

When an explicit expression exists for the c.d.f., as is the case for either form of the geometric distribution, for instance, the alternative formula (2.4) provides an easy way of calculating the mean of a distribution. However, this happens only rarely for discrete random variables; the continuous analogue, which is discussed in Section 4, is a much more useful result.

If you are interested in seeing how to apply (2.4) to find the mean of a geometric distribution, or wish to try this for yourself, then refer to Exercise 9.6.

2.4 Variance

The mean of a random variable gives a measure of its average value. A measure of the spread of X is given by the **variance**. This is the expected value of $(X - \mu)^2$, where $\mu = E(X)$.

In general, the mean of a function g of a random variable X may be calculated by using the formula

$$E[g(X)] = \sum_{x \in \Omega_X} g(x)\, p_X(x). \tag{2.5}$$

The variance is therefore given by

$$E[(X - \mu)^2] = \sum_{x \in \Omega_X} (x - \mu)^2\, p(x).$$

The variance of X is denoted by $V(X)$ or σ^2.

The symbol σ is pronounced 'sigma'.

Calculation of expectations is often simplified by using the result

$$E\left[\sum_{i=1}^{k} a_i\, g_i(X)\right] = \sum_{i=1}^{k} a_i\, E[g_i(X)], \tag{2.6}$$

where each a_i $(i = 1, \ldots, k)$ is a constant. This enables the calculation of an expectation of a complicated function of X to be split up into the sum of simpler calculations. An alternative formula for the variance can be obtained as follows using (2.6):

$$
\begin{aligned}
V(X) &= E[(X - \mu)^2] \\
&= E(X^2 - 2\mu X + \mu^2) \\
&= E(X^2) - 2\mu E(X) + \mu^2, \quad \text{using (2.6),} \\
&= E(X^2) - \mu^2.
\end{aligned}
$$

For any constant c,
$$E(c) = c.$$
This result has been used here.

The **standard deviation** of X, which is denoted by σ, is defined to be the square root of the variance:

$$\sigma = \sqrt{V(X)}.$$

The formulas for the variance and standard deviation of a discrete random variable are summarised in the following box.

The variance of a discrete random variable

For a discrete random variable X with p.m.f. $p(x)$ and mean $\mu = E(X)$, the **variance** of X, which is denoted by σ^2 or $V(X)$, is given by

$$\sigma^2 = V(X) = E[(X - \mu)^2] = \sum_{x \in \Omega_X} (x - \mu)^2\, p(x). \tag{2.7}$$

Equivalently, the variance is given by

$$\sigma^2 = V(X) = E(X^2) - \mu^2. \tag{2.8}$$

The **standard deviation** of X is the square root of the variance.

Example 2.7   The variance of a Bernoulli distribution

Suppose that the random variable X has a Bernoulli distribution with parameter p: $X \sim B(1, p)$. In this case, as in many situations, it is simpler to use (2.8) than (2.7) to find the variance. Using (2.5) with $g(x) = x^2$,

$$
\begin{aligned}
E(X^2) = \sum x^2 p(x) &= 0^2 \times p(0) + 1^2 \times p(1) \\
&= 0^2 \times q + 1^2 \times p \\
&= p.
\end{aligned}
$$

From Example 2.5, $\mu = E(X) = p$, so, using (2.8), the variance of X is

$$V(X) = E(X^2) - \mu^2 = p - p^2 = p(1 - p) = pq.$$

The standard deviation of X is $\sqrt{V(X)} = \sqrt{pq}$. ◆

Activity 2.12   Calculating a variance

Calculate the variance of the random variable X of Activity 2.10.

To complete this section, two results concerning the mean and variance of a sum of two random variables X and Y are stated without proof.

The mean and variance of $X + Y$

For any two random variables X and Y,

$$E(X + Y) = E(X) + E(Y). \tag{2.9}$$

If X and Y are independent, then

$$V(X + Y) = V(X) + V(Y). \tag{2.10}$$

Result (2.9) says that the mean of the sum of any two random variables is equal to the sum of their means. Result (2.10) says that if, in addition, the random variables are independent, then the variance of their sum is equal to the sum of their variances.

Activity 2.13   The mean and variance of a sum

Find the mean and variance of the sum of the following pairs of independent random variables X and Y.

(a) $X \sim \text{Poisson}(\mu_1)$, $Y \sim \text{Poisson}(\mu_2)$.

(b) $X \sim G_1\left(\frac{1}{3}\right)$, $Y \sim G_1\left(\frac{1}{3}\right)$.

The means and variances of standard discrete distributions are given in the table of discrete probability distributions in the *Handbook* (Table 8). You may quote the results given in this table.

Some of these results are derived in Section 3.

Summary of Section 2

The probability mass function (p.m.f.) and the cumulative distribution function (c.d.f.) of a discrete random variable have been defined in this section, and formulas for the mean and variance have been given. You have seen that an alternative formula for the mean, which involves the c.d.f., can be used when the range of the random variable is a subset of $\{0, 1, \ldots\}$.

Several families of distributions have been reviewed briefly: discrete uniform, Bernoulli, binomial, Poisson, geometric starting at 0 and geometric starting at 1, negative binomial with range $\{0, 1, \ldots\}$ and negative binomial with range $\{k, k + 1, \ldots\}$.

Two results for sums of random variables have been discussed: the expected value of a sum of random variables is equal to the sum of their expected values; and if, in addition, the random variables are independent, then the variance of their sum is equal to the sum of their variances. These results have been introduced for discrete random variables, but they also hold for continuous random variables.

Exercises on Section 2

Exercise 2.1   Binomial coefficients

Find the values of the following binomial coefficients.

(a) $\begin{pmatrix} 6 \\ 1 \end{pmatrix}$ (b) $\begin{pmatrix} 7 \\ 2 \end{pmatrix}$ (c) $\begin{pmatrix} 11 \\ 9 \end{pmatrix}$ (d) $\begin{pmatrix} 9 \\ 6 \end{pmatrix}$

Exercise 2.2   *Binomial probabilities*

(a) If $X \sim B(6, 0.6)$, find $P(X = 2)$.

(b) If $Y \sim B(7, 0.2)$, find $P(Y < 3)$.

(c) If $Z \sim B(10, 0.9)$, find $P(Z > 8)$.

Exercise 2.3   *Poisson probabilities*

(a) If $X \sim \text{Poisson}(1.8)$, find $P(X = 4)$.

(b) If $Y \sim \text{Poisson}(4)$, find ~~$P(X \geq 3)$~~. $P(Y \geq 3)$

Exercise 2.4   *Poisson's approximation for rare events*

If $X \sim B(300, 0.02)$, find an approximate value for $P(X \leq 3)$.

Exercise 2.5   *Choosing a probability model*

In a sequence of independent Bernoulli trials, the probability of success in each trial is 0.03. The random variables A, B, C and D are defined as follows.

> A: the number of successes in a sequence of six trials.
>
> B: the number of trials up to and including the first success.
>
> C: the number of successes that occur before the third failure.
>
> D: the number of successes in a sequence of 150 trials.

(a) Write down the probability distributions of A, B and C.

(b) Write down the distribution that can be used to approximate the distribution of D.

Exercise 2.6   *Means and variances*

The probability distributions of the random variables X and Y are given in Tables 2.4 and 2.5.

Table 2.4   The p.m.f. of X

x	0	1	2	3
$p(x)$	0.4	0.2	0.3	0.1

Table 2.5   The p.m.f. of Y

y	1	2	3	4
$p(y)$	0.5	0.3	0.1	0.1

(a) Find the mean and variance of X.

(b) Use the alternative formula for the mean (2.4) to find the expected value of Y.

3   Probability generating functions

In this section, a function called the *probability generating function* (p.g.f.) is introduced. This function encapsulates the distribution of a random variable in a concise mathematical form. The p.g.f. is an important mathematical tool in the study of random processes. It is used frequently from *Book 3* onwards. The p.g.f. is defined in Subsection 3.1, and some of its properties are discussed. The p.g.f.s of some standard discrete distributions are discussed in Subsection 3.2. Using a p.g.f. provides a way of calculating the mean and variance of a distribution without having to sum series: this method is described in Subsection 3.3. In Subsection 3.4, you will see how p.g.f.s can be used to find the distribution of a sum of independent random variables. The p.g.f. of a constant multiple of a random variable is discussed in Subsection 3.5.

3.1   The probability generating function

The **probability generating function** (p.g.f.) is defined for any discrete random variable X whose range is a subset of $\{0, 1, 2, \ldots\}$. It is denoted by $\Pi_X(s)$, but the subscript X is often omitted if this does not lead to any ambiguity. Its definition is given in the following box.

In prob theory, the prob generating function of a discrete random variable is a power series representation (the generating function) of the probability mass function of the random variable

---

The probability generating function

The **probability generating function** (p.g.f.) of a discrete random variable X with p.m.f. $p(x)$, whose range is a subset of $\{0, 1, 2, \ldots\}$, is given by

$$\Pi(s) = \sum_{x=0}^{\infty} p(x)\, s^x. \tag{3.1}$$

That is,

$$\Pi(s) = p(0) + p(1)\, s + p(2)\, s^2 + \cdots + p(x)\, s^x + \cdots .$$

Note that s is not a random variable: it is a dummy variable and has no particular interpretation. Another letter could just as well be used instead of s.

It is generally assumed that $|s| \leq 1$.

As you can see from the definition, the p.g.f. $\Pi(s)$ is either a polynomial or a power series in s, and the coefficient of s^x is $p(x) = P(X = x)$. Given a p.m.f. $p(x)$, the p.g.f. is obtained simply by writing down the series in which the constant term is $p(0)$, the coefficient of s is $p(1)$, the coefficient of s^2 is $p(2)$, and so on.

Example 3.1   Writing down p.g.f.s

The random variables X and Y have the p.m.f.s given in Tables 3.1 and 3.2.

Table 3.1   The p.m.f. of X

x	1	2
$p(x)$	0.6	0.4

Table 3.2   The p.m.f. of Y

y	0	1	2
$p(y)$	0.2	0.6	0.2

The p.g.f. of X is

$$\Pi(s) = 0.6s + 0.4s^2.$$

The p.g.f. of Y is

$$\Pi(s) = 0.2 + 0.6s + 0.2s^2. \quad \blacklozenge$$

Activity 3.1   Writing down p.g.f.s

Write down the p.g.f. of each of the following random variables.

(a) The random variable X with the p.m.f. in Table 3.3.

(b) The random variable X where X is the number obtained when a fair six-sided die is rolled.

(c) The random variable X that takes the value 7 with probability 1.

Table 3.3   The p.m.f. of X

x	1	2	3
$p(x)$	0.5	0.4	0.1

A random variable that takes a single value with probability 1 is called **degenerate**. The random variable in part (c) of Activity 3.1, which takes the value 7 with probability 1, is an example of a degenerate random variable. In general, if a random variable X takes the value k with probability 1, then

$$p(k) = P(X = k) = 1,$$
$$p(x) = P(X = x) = 0 \quad \text{for } x \neq k,$$

so the p.g.f. of X is

$$\Pi(s) = s^k.$$

This result is used in *Books 4 and 5*.

Given a p.g.f. $\Pi(s)$, the probability $p(x) = P(X = x)$ can be obtained for any particular value of x by finding the coefficient of s^x in $\Pi(s)$. This is illustrated in Example 3.2.

Example 3.2 Obtaining the p.m.f. from the p.g.f.

Suppose that the p.g.f. of X is

$$\Pi(s) = \tfrac{1}{4}(1 + s)^2.$$

This can be rewritten as

$$\Pi(s) = \tfrac{1}{4} + \tfrac{1}{2}s + \tfrac{1}{4}s^2,$$

so

$$p(0) = \tfrac{1}{4}, \quad p(1) = \tfrac{1}{2}, \quad p(2) = \tfrac{1}{4}. \quad \blacklozenge$$

Activity 3.2 Obtaining the p.m.f. from the p.g.f.

Find the p.m.f.s of the random variables with the following p.g.f.s.

(a) $\Pi(s) = \tfrac{1}{4}s(1 + s + 2s^2)$

(b) $\Pi(s) = \tfrac{1}{9}(2 + s^2)^2$

You have seen how to obtain the p.g.f. given the p.m.f. of a random variable, and how to reconstruct a p.m.f. from a p.g.f. Before you look at the p.g.f.s of some standard distributions, some of the basic properties of p.g.f.s will be discussed briefly.

Suppose that $\Pi(s)$ is the p.g.f. of a random variable X:

$$\Pi(s) = \sum_{x=0}^{\infty} p(x)\, s^x = p(0) + p(1)\, s + p(2)\, s^2 + \cdots.$$

First note that putting $s = 0$ gives

$$\Pi(0) = p(0) + 0 + 0 + \cdots = p(0),$$

so

$$\Pi(0) = p(0) = P(X = 0).$$

Putting $s = 1$ in the definition of $\Pi(s)$ gives

$$\Pi(1) = p(0) + p(1) + p(2) + \cdots.$$

For a p.m.f., the sum of the probabilities of all the possible values is equal to 1, so $\Pi(1) = 1$.

For each x, the coefficient of s^x in the p.g.f. is $p(x)$. Thus the p.m.f. determines the p.g.f. uniquely, and vice versa. No information is lost when a p.g.f. is found: the original distribution can be reconstructed from it. This is what makes the p.g.f. so useful.

These properties are summarised in the following box.

Properties of the p.g.f.

◇   The coefficient of s^x in $\Pi(s)$ is $p(x)$:

$$\Pi(s) = \sum_{x=0}^{\infty} p(x)\, s^x = p(0) + p(1)\, s + p(2)\, s^2 + \cdots.$$

◇   The p.g.f. determines a distribution uniquely, and vice versa.

◇ $\Pi(0) = p(0) = P(X = 0)$.

◇ $\Pi(1) = 1$.

3.2   The p.g.f.s of standard distributions

Formulas for the p.g.f.s of some standard distributions are given in the *Handbook*. In this subsection, some of these formulas are derived, and you will see how they can be used to write down the p.g.f. of a random variable and to identify the distribution of a random variable from its p.g.f.

See Table 8 in the *Handbook*.

Example 3.3   The p.g.f. of a geometric distribution $G_1(p)$

If $X \sim G_1(p)$, then the p.m.f. of X is

$$p(x) = q^{x-1}p, \quad x = 1, 2, \dots .$$

The p.g.f. of X is given by

$$\begin{aligned}
\Pi(s) &= \sum_{x=0}^{\infty} p(x)\, s^x \\
&= \sum_{x=1}^{\infty} q^{x-1} p s^x \\
&= p(s + qs^2 + q^2 s^3 + q^3 s^4 + \cdots) \\
&= ps(1 + qs + (qs)^2 + (qs)^3 + \cdots).
\end{aligned}$$

The series in parentheses is a geometric progression in powers of qs. Its sum is $1/(1 - qs)$ (provided that $|qs| < 1$). Hence the p.g.f. of a geometric distribution starting at 1 and with parameter p is

$$\Pi(s) = \frac{ps}{1 - qs}. \quad \blacklozenge$$

Recall that, for $|x| < 1$,

$$1 + x + x^2 + \cdots = \frac{1}{1 - x}.$$

Under the general assumption that $|s| \leq 1$, it follows that $|qs| < 1$.

Activity 3.3   The p.g.f. of a geometric distribution $G_0(p)$

Find the p.g.f. of X, where $X \sim G_0(p)$.

Example 3.4   The p.g.f. of a binomial distribution

Suppose that $X \sim B(n,p)$. Then the p.m.f. of X is

$$p(x) = \binom{n}{x} p^x q^{n-x}, \quad x = 0, 1, \ldots, n.$$

The p.g.f. of X is given by

$$
\begin{aligned}
\Pi(s) &= \sum_{x=0}^{\infty} p(x)\, s^x \\
&= \sum_{x=0}^{n} \binom{n}{x} p^x q^{n-x} s^x \\
&= \sum_{x=0}^{n} \binom{n}{x} (ps)^x q^{n-x} \\
&= (q + ps)^n, \quad \text{by the binomial theorem.}
\end{aligned}
$$

Thus the p.g.f. of the binomial distribution with parameters n and p is

$$\Pi(s) = (q + ps)^n. \quad \blacklozenge$$

A statement of the binomial theorem is given in the *Handbook*.

Activity 3.4   The p.g.f. of a Poisson distribution

Show that the p.g.f. of a Poisson distribution with parameter μ is given by

$$\Pi(s) = e^{-\mu(1-s)}.$$

$$\left(\text{Hint: } e^{\theta} = 1 + \theta + \frac{\theta^2}{2!} + \cdots + \frac{\theta^n}{n!} + \cdots. \right)$$

The p.g.f.s of some standard distributions are given in Table 3.4. The entries in this table are also given in the table of discrete probability distributions in the *Handbook* (Table 8).

Table 3.4   Probability generating functions of some standard distributions

Distribution	p.m.f.	Range	p.g.f.
Bernoulli, $B(1,p)$	$p^x q^{1-x}$	$0, 1$	$q + ps$
Binomial, $B(n,p)$	$\binom{n}{x} p^x q^{n-x}$	$0, 1, \ldots, n$	$(q + ps)^n$
Poisson(μ)	$\dfrac{e^{-\mu}\mu^x}{x!}$	$0, 1, \ldots$	$e^{-\mu(1-s)}$
Geometric, $G_1(p)$	$q^{x-1} p$	$1, 2, \ldots$	$\dfrac{ps}{1 - qs}$
Negative binomial	$\binom{x-1}{r-1} q^{x-r} p^r$	$r, r+1, \ldots$	$\left(\dfrac{ps}{1 - qs}\right)^r$
Geometric, $G_0(p)$	$p^x q$	$0, 1, \ldots$	$\dfrac{q}{1 - ps}$
Negative binomial	$\binom{r+x-1}{r-1} p^x q^r$	$0, 1, \ldots$	$\left(\dfrac{q}{1 - ps}\right)^r$

The results in this table may be quoted whenever they are required. They can be used either to write down the p.g.f. of a distribution or to identify a distribution. Examples 3.5 and 3.6 illustrate how this is done.

Example 3.5   Writing down the p.g.f.

Suppose that $X \sim B\left(6, \frac{2}{3}\right)$ and $Y \sim G_0\left(\frac{2}{5}\right)$.

If $X \sim B(n, p)$, then the p.g.f. of X is

$$\Pi_X(s) = (q + ps)^n.$$

Putting $n = 6$, $p = \frac{2}{3}$ and $q = \frac{1}{3}$ in this formula gives the p.g.f. of the binomial distribution $B\left(6, \frac{2}{3}\right)$:

$$\Pi_X(s) = \left(\frac{1}{3} + \frac{2}{3}s\right)^6.$$

If $Y \sim G_0(p)$, then the p.g.f. of Y is

$$\Pi_Y(s) = \frac{q}{1 - ps}.$$

Putting $p = \frac{2}{5}$ and $q = \frac{3}{5}$ in this formula gives the p.g.f. of the geometric distribution $G_0\left(\frac{2}{5}\right)$:

$$\Pi_Y(s) = \frac{\frac{3}{5}}{1 - \frac{2}{5}s} = \frac{3}{5 - 2s}. \quad \blacklozenge$$

Activity 3.5   Writing down the p.g.f.

Write down the p.g.f. of each of the following random variables.

(a) $X \sim \text{Poisson}(4)$ (b) $Y \sim G_1\left(\frac{1}{3}\right)$

$\Pi(s) = e^{-4(1-s)}$

$\Pi(s) = \frac{\frac{1}{3}s}{1 - \frac{2}{3}s} = \frac{s}{3 - 2s}$

Example 3.6   Identifying the distribution from the p.g.f.

Suppose that the p.g.f.s of the random variables X and Y are

$$\Pi_X(s) = \frac{3s}{4 - s}, \quad \Pi_Y(s) = \frac{1}{(4 - 3s)^3}.$$

How can the distributions of X and Y be identified?

The distribution of a random variable can be identified from its p.g.f. by rewriting it so that its form matches one of those in Table 3.4.

The p.g.f. of X is similar to that of a geometric distribution with range $\{1, 2, \ldots\}$, but with the number 4 in the denominator instead of 1. Dividing numerator and denominator by 4 gives

$$\Pi_X(s) = \frac{3s}{4 - s} = \frac{\frac{3}{4}s}{1 - \frac{1}{4}s}.$$

This is the p.g.f. of a geometric distribution $G_1(p)$ with $p = \frac{3}{4}$, so $X \sim G_1\left(\frac{3}{4}\right)$.

The p.g.f. of Y is similar to that of a negative binomial distribution with range $\{0, 1, \ldots\}$, and parameters r and p, but with 4 in the denominator instead of 1. The p.g.f. can be rewritten as

$$\Pi_Y(s) = \left(\frac{1}{4 - 3s}\right)^3 = \left(\frac{\frac{1}{4}}{1 - \frac{3}{4}s}\right)^3.$$

Thus Y has a negative binomial distribution with range starting at 0, and parameters $r = 3$ and $p = \frac{3}{4}$.

Note that to identify a distribution, the values of the parameters must be given, and in the case of the geometric and negative binomial distributions, the range must also be stated. $\blacklozenge$

Activity 3.6   Identifying the distribution from the p.g.f.

For each of the following p.g.f.s, identify the corresponding probability distribution.

(a) $\Pi(s) = \frac{1}{81}(2+s)^4$ (b) $\Pi(s) = e^{-\frac{1}{3}(1-s)t}$

(c) $\Pi(s) = \dfrac{1}{5-4s}$ (d) $\Pi(s) = \dfrac{4}{(3-s)^2}$

3.3 Calculating means and variances

In Subsections 2.3 and 2.4, the mean and variance of a discrete random variable X were found using the formulas

$$\mu = E(X) = \sum_{x\in\Omega_X} x\,p(x), \tag{3.2}$$

$$\sigma^2 = V(X) = E(X^2) - \mu^2 = \sum_{x\in\Omega_X} x^2 p(x) - \mu^2. \tag{3.3}$$

In this subsection, formulas are derived for obtaining the mean and variance of a random variable whose range is a subset of $\{0,1,\ldots\}$ from its p.g.f. You will not be expected to reproduce these derivations, just to use the formulas.

The p.g.f. of a random variable X is

$$\Pi(s) = \sum_{x=0}^{\infty} p(x)\,s^x = p(0) + p(1)\,s + p(2)\,s^2 + p(3)\,s^3 + \cdots.$$

See Formula (3.1).

Differentiating this with respect to s gives

$$\Pi'(s) = \sum_{x=0}^{\infty} x\,p(x)\,s^{x-1} = p(1) + 2\,p(2)\,s + 3\,p(3)\,s^2 + \cdots.$$

Putting $s = 1$ leads to

$$\Pi'(1) = \sum_{x=0}^{\infty} x\,p(x) = p(1) + 2\,p(2) + 3\,p(3) + \cdots = E(X).$$

Hence

$$\mu = E(X) = \Pi'(1).$$

Differentiating $\Pi(s)$ a second time with respect to s gives

$$\Pi''(s) = \sum_{x=0}^{\infty} x(x-1)\,p(x)\,s^{x-2}.$$

Putting $s = 1$ leads to

$$\Pi''(1) = \sum_{x=0}^{\infty} x(x-1)\,p(x)$$
$$= \sum_{x=0}^{\infty} x^2\,p(x) - \sum_{x=0}^{\infty} x\,p(x)$$
$$= E(X^2) - E(X)$$
$$= E(X^2) - \mu.$$

Hence

$$E(X^2) = \Pi''(1) + \mu.$$

But $\sigma^2 = V(X) = E(X^2) - \mu^2$, so

$$\sigma^2 = V(X) = \Pi''(1) + \mu - \mu^2.$$

The formulas just obtained are stated in the following box.

Formulas for obtaining the mean and variance from the p.g.f.

If X is a random variable with p.g.f. $\Pi(s)$, then the mean and variance of X may be found using the formulas

$$\mu = E(X) = \Pi'(1), \tag{3.4}$$

$$\sigma^2 = V(X) = \Pi''(1) + \mu - \mu^2. \tag{3.5}$$

Formulas (3.4) and (3.5) provide a method of calculating the mean and the variance of any random variable whose p.g.f. exists. It is much easier to use these formulas to find the means and variances of many of the standard distributions than it is to use the definitions (3.2) and (3.3) directly. Their use is illustrated in Example 3.7.

Example 3.7   The mean and variance of a binomial distribution

If $X \sim B(n, p)$, then the p.g.f. of X is

$$\Pi(s) = (q + ps)^n.$$

Differentiating the p.g.f. twice with respect to s gives

$$\Pi'(s) = np \, (q + ps)^{n-1},$$

$$\Pi''(s) = n(n-1)p^2(q + ps)^{n-2}.$$

Hence

$$\Pi'(1) = np(q + p)^{n-1} = np(1)^{n-1} = np,$$

$$\Pi''(1) = n(n-1)p^2(q + p)^{n-2} = n(n-1)p^2(1)^{n-2} = n(n-1)p^2.$$

Using Formulas (3.4) and (3.5) gives

$$\mu = \Pi'(1) = np,$$

$$\begin{aligned}
\sigma^2 &= \Pi''(1) + \mu - \mu^2 \\
&= n(n-1)p^2 + np - n^2p^2 \\
&= n^2p^2 - np^2 + np - n^2p^2 \\
&= np - np^2 \\
&= np(1 - p) \\
&= npq. \quad \blacklozenge
\end{aligned}$$

Activity 3.7   Finding the mean and variance

Use the p.g.f. to find the mean and variance of each of the following distributions.

(a) Poisson(μ) (b) $G_1(p)$

The means and variances of standard distributions are given in Table 8 in the *Handbook*. You may quote such results whenever they are required. However, for any non-standard distribution, you will need to use either the definitions given in Section 2 or Formulas (3.4) and (3.5). If the p.g.f. has a succinct form, then using Formulas (3.4) and (3.5) is usually the simpler of the two methods.

3.4   *Sums of independent random variables*

The mean and variance of the sum of two independent random variables can be found using (2.9) and (2.10). But how can the distribution of the sum be found? Suppose that X and Y are two such variates, the range of each being a subset of $\{0, 1, \ldots\}$, and that $Z = X + Y$.

The p.m.f. of Z could be found directly as follows:

$$p_Z(0) = P(Z = 0) = P(X = 0 \text{ and } Y = 0) = p_X(0)\, p_Y(0),$$
$$\begin{aligned} p_Z(1) = P(Z = 1) &= P([X = 0 \text{ and } Y = 1] \text{ or } [X = 1 \text{ and } Y = 0]) \\ &= p_X(0)\, p_Y(1) + p_X(1)\, p_Y(0), \end{aligned}$$

and so on. Clearly, except for simple cases, the work involved could be considerable using this approach.

In general, it is much simpler to find the p.g.f. of Z in terms of the p.g.f.s of X and Y, and then to identify the distribution of Z from its p.g.f. In order to do this, a general result is required, the derivation of which depends on the following neat mathematical definition of the p.g.f., which is equivalent to that given in Subsection 3.1.

The p.g.f. of a discrete random variable X whose range is a subset of $\{0, 1, \ldots\}$ may also be defined as the expectation of the function $g(X) = s^X$; that is,

$$\Pi(s) = E\left(s^X\right). \tag{3.6}$$

In Section 2, the expectation of a function g of a random variable X with p.m.f. $p(x)$ was defined by the formula

$$E[g(X)] = \sum_{x \in \Omega_X} g(x)\, p(x).$$

Hence

$$E\left(s^X\right) = \sum_{x \in \Omega_X} s^x\, p(x) = \sum_{x=0}^{\infty} p(x)\, s^x.$$

Therefore the definition of the p.g.f. in (3.6) is equivalent to the definition (3.1); that is,

$$\Pi(s) = E\left(s^X\right) = \sum_{x=0}^{\infty} p(x)\, s^x.$$

Using (3.6), the p.g.f. of $Z = X + Y$ can be found as follows.

Let $\Pi_X(s)$, $\Pi_Y(s)$ and $\Pi_Z(s)$ denote the p.g.f.s of X, Y and Z, respectively. Then

$$\Pi_X(s) = E\left(s^X\right), \quad \Pi_Y(s) = E\left(s^Y\right), \quad \Pi_Z(s) = E\left(s^Z\right).$$

Since $Z = X + Y$,

$$\Pi_Z(s) = E\left(s^Z\right) = E\left(s^{X+Y}\right) = E\left(s^X s^Y\right).$$

For any functions $g(X)$ and $h(Y)$ of independent random variables X and Y,

$$E[g(X)\, h(Y)] = E[g(X)]\, E[h(Y)].$$

It is straightforward to show this.

Therefore, since X and Y are independent,

$$E\left(s^X s^Y\right) = E\left(s^X\right) E\left(s^Y\right),$$

and hence

$$\Pi_Z(s) = E\left(s^X\right) E\left(s^Y\right) = \Pi_X(s)\, \Pi_Y(s).$$

This result is stated formally in the following box.

The p.g.f. of the sum of two independent random variables

If X and Y are independent random variables, then the p.g.f. of their sum, Z, is the product of their p.g.f.s:

$$\Pi_Z(s) = \Pi_X(s)\,\Pi_Y(s). \tag{3.7}$$

Example 3.8   A sum of independent binomial variates

If X and Y are independent and $X \sim B(m,p)$, $Y \sim B(n,p)$, then

$$\Pi_X(s) = (q + ps)^m \quad \text{and} \quad \Pi_Y(s) = (q + ps)^n.$$

Therefore the p.g.f. of $Z = X + Y$ is

$$\Pi_Z(s) = (q + ps)^m (q + ps)^n = (q + ps)^{m+n},$$

and hence $Z \sim B(m + n, p)$.   ◆

Activity 3.8   A sum of independent Poisson variates

If X and Y are independent Poisson variates with parameters μ_1 and μ_2, find the p.g.f. of $Z = X + Y$, and hence identify the distribution of Z.

Result (3.7) can also be used to write a random variable as a sum of two simpler independent random variables, as in Example 3.9.

Example 3.9   Recurrent events

A model for events that occur repeatedly is described in *Book 5*. The p.g.f. of W_r, the waiting time until the rth event, is

$$\Pi(s) = \left(\tfrac{1}{2}s + \tfrac{1}{2}s^2\right)^r.$$

In particular, the p.g.f. of W_6, the waiting time until the sixth event, is

$$\Pi(s) = \left(\tfrac{1}{2}s + \tfrac{1}{2}s^2\right)^6,$$

which can be rewritten as

$$\Pi(s) = s^6\left(\tfrac{1}{2} + \tfrac{1}{2}s\right)^6.$$

This is the product of two p.g.f.s, s^6 and $\left(\tfrac{1}{2} + \tfrac{1}{2}s\right)^6$, so W_6 is the sum of two independent random variables. Since s^6 is the p.g.f. of a degenerate random variable X that takes the value 6 with probability 1, and $\left(\tfrac{1}{2} + \tfrac{1}{2}s\right)^6$ is the p.g.f. of a binomial variate Y with parameters 6 and $\tfrac{1}{2}$,

$$W_6 = 6 + Y, \quad \text{where } Y \sim B\left(6, \tfrac{1}{2}\right).$$

In this case, expressing the waiting time as a sum of two other random variables makes it possible to calculate probabilities associated with the waiting time much more easily than would otherwise be the case.   ◆

Activity 3.9   A sum of two independent variates

The random variable Z may be regarded as the sum of two independent random variables, one of which has a binomial distribution. The p.g.f. of Z is

$$\Pi_Z(s) = (0.6s^2 + 0.4s^3)^4.$$

Identify the two random variables.

Result (3.7) extends to any fixed number of independent discrete random variables.

The p.g.f. of a sum of n independent random variables

If $Z = X_1 + X_2 + \cdots + X_n$, where $X_1, X_2, \ldots, X_n$ are independent discrete variates with p.g.f.s $\Pi_{X_1}(s), \Pi_{X_2}(s), \ldots, \Pi_{X_n}(s)$, then

$$\Pi_Z(s) = \Pi_{X_1}(s) \times \Pi_{X_2}(s) \times \cdots \times \Pi_{X_n}(s). \tag{3.8}$$

Example 3.10   A sum of independent Bernoulli variates

If $X_1, X_2, \ldots, X_n$ are independent Bernoulli variates, $X_i \sim B(1, p)$, $i = 1, 2, \ldots, n$, then the p.g.f. of $Z = X_1 + X_2 + \cdots + X_n$ is

$$\Pi_Z(s) = (q + ps)(q + ps) \cdots (q + ps)$$
$$= (q + ps)^n.$$

This is the p.g.f. of a binomial distribution with parameters n and p. So the sum of n independent Bernoulli variates with parameter p has the binomial distribution $B(n, p)$. This confirms a result given in Subsection 2.2. ◆

Activity 3.10   A sum of independent geometric variates

If $X_1, X_2, \ldots, X_n$ are independent $G_0(p)$ variates, find the p.g.f. of $Z = X_1 + X_2 + \cdots + X_n$, and hence identify the distribution of Z.

The results given at the end of Section 2 for the mean and variance of two independent random variables can also be derived using p.g.f.s. You may like to try this. (You will need to differentiate Formula (3.7) and use Formulas (3.4) and (3.5).) These results generalise to sums of more than two random variables in an obvious way:

$$E(X_1 + \cdots + X_n) = E(X_1) + \cdots + E(X_n)$$

and, if $X_1, \ldots, X_n$ are independent,

$$V(X_1 + \cdots + X_n) = V(X_1) + \cdots + V(X_n).$$

In fact, many of the results obtained for the expectation of functions of discrete random variables also hold for continuous random variables. In general, such results will be stated and used for continuous random variables without proof.

Continuous random variables are discussed in Sections 4 and 5.

3.5 The p.g.f. of a constant multiple

If the random variable X has p.g.f. $\Pi_X(s)$ then, by the definition in (3.6),

$$\Pi_X(s) = E\left(s^X\right).$$

Suppose that the random variable Y is a constant multiple of X, that is, $Y = kX$ where k is a positive integer. Then, using (3.6),

$$\Pi_Y(s) = E\left(s^Y\right) = E\left(s^{kX}\right) = E\left[(s^k)^X\right] = \Pi_X(s^k).$$

That is, the p.g.f. of $Y = kX$ is obtained by replacing s with s^k in the p.g.f. of X. This result is stated in the following box.

The p.g.f. of a constant multiple

If the random variable X has p.g.f. $\Pi_X(s)$, then $\Pi_Y(s)$, the p.g.f. of $Y = kX$ ($k = 1, 2, \ldots$), is given by

$$\Pi_Y(s) = \Pi_X(s^k). \tag{3.9}$$

This result is used in *Book 5*.

Example 3.11   A constant multiple

If $X \sim G_1(0.5)$, then

$$\Pi_X(s) = \frac{0.5s}{1 - 0.5s}.$$

$$\frac{p^s}{1 - qs}$$

Using (3.9), the p.g.f. of $Y = 3X$ is obtained by replacing s with s^3 in $\Pi_X(s)$, so

$$\Pi_Y(s) = \frac{0.5s^3}{1 - 0.5s^3}. \quad \blacklozenge$$

Activity 3.11   Constant multiples

(a) If $X \sim G_0(0.4)$, obtain the p.g.f. of $Y = 5X$.

(b) Suppose that the p.g.f. of X is given by

$$\Pi_X(s) = \frac{2 + s}{5 - 2s}.$$

Write down the p.g.f. of $Y = 2X$.

Summary of Section 3

In this section, the p.g.f. of a discrete random variable has been defined and you have seen how it can be used to find the mean and variance of a distribution. You have also seen how p.g.f.s can be used to find the distribution of a sum of independent discrete random variables.

Exercises on Section 3

Exercise 3.1   Probability generating functions

Write down the p.g.f. of each of the following random variables.

(a) $X \sim B(10, 0.6)$

(b) $X \sim G_0(0.7)$

(c) X has a negative binomial distribution with parameters 3 and $\frac{5}{8}$, and range $\{3, 4, \ldots\}$.

(d) X takes the value 5 with probability 1.

Exercise 3.2   Standard distributions

For each of the following p.g.f.s, identify the distribution (including the values of any parameters) and use the formulas given in Table 8 in the *Handbook* to find the mean and variance.

(a) $\dfrac{5}{7 - 2s}$ (b) $\dfrac{5s}{7 - 2s}$ (c) $\left(\dfrac{2}{7 - 5s}\right)^2$

(d) $\left(\dfrac{2s}{7 - 5s}\right)^3$ (e) $\left(\dfrac{9 + s}{10}\right)^7$ (f) $\cdot e^{-3(1-s)/4}$

Exercise 3.3   Using the p.g.f.

The p.g.f. of the random variable X is

$$\Pi(s) = \frac{4}{5 - s^2}.$$

(a) Find the values of each of the following.

   (i) $P(X = 0)$ (ii) $E(X)$ (iii) $V(X)$

(b) Write $\Pi(s)$ as a power series in s. Hence find the range of X and write down the probabilities $p(0)$, $p(1)$, $p(2)$, $p(3)$ and $p(4)$.

Exercise 3.4   Sums and multiples of random variables

(a) The p.g.f.s of the random variables X and Y, which are independent, are

$$\Pi_X(s) = \tfrac{1}{4}(1 + s)^2, \quad \Pi_Y(s) = e^{-2(1-s)}.$$

Write down the p.g.f.s of the random variables U, V and W, where

   (i) $U = X + Y$,   (ii) $V = 2X$,   (iii) $W = 3Y$.

(b) The random variable Z may be regarded as the sum of two independent random variables, one of which has a binomial distribution. The p.g.f. of Z is

$$\Pi_Z(s) = \tfrac{1}{81}s^2(2 + s)^4.$$

Identify the two random variables.

4 Continuous random variables

In this section, the basic concepts associated with continuous random variables are discussed. In Subsection 4.1, the concept of the cumulative distribution function is extended to continuous random variables, the probability density function is introduced, and these functions are used to calculate probabilities. Expectation for continuous random variables is discussed in Subsection 4.2.

4.1 Cumulative distribution functions and probability density functions

The concept of the cumulative distribution function was defined in Section 2 for a discrete random variable. The definition also applies for continuous random variables. If X is a continuous variate, then $F(x)$, its **cumulative distribution function** (c.d.f.), is defined by

$$F(x) = P(X \le x), \quad x \in \mathbb{R}.$$

If there is any possibility of confusion, the random variable is included as a subscript: $F_X(x)$.

Some properties of the c.d.f. follow immediately from the definition. For instance, for every value of x, $F(x)$ is a probability, so its value lies between 0 and 1 (inclusive). Also, when $x_1 < x_2$, $P(X \le x_1) \le P(X \le x_2)$, so $F(x_1) \le F(x_2)$. Thus a c.d.f. is a non-decreasing function with values between 0 and 1. And since a random variable must take some value between $-\infty$ and ∞, $F(x) \to 1$ as $x \to \infty$, and $F(x) \to 0$ as $x \to -\infty$.

The basic properties of c.d.f.s, which apply for both discrete and continuous random variables, are summarised in the following box.

Properties of cumulative distribution functions

The c.d.f. F of a random variable X, which is defined for all $x \in \mathbb{R}$ by $F(x) = P(X \le x)$, has the following properties.

$\diamond$ $0 \le F(x) \le 1, x \in \mathbb{R}$.

$\diamond$ For any x_1 and x_2 such that $x_1 < x_2$,
$$F(x_1) \le F(x_2).$$

$\diamond$ $\lim\limits_{x \to -\infty} F(x) = 0$ and $\lim\limits_{x \to \infty} F(x) = 1$.

Example 4.1 Using the c.d.f.

The c.d.f. $F(x)$ of a random variable X that takes values between 1 and 2 is given by

$$F(x) = \begin{cases} 0, & x < 1, \\ \frac{1}{3}(x^2 - 1), & 1 \le x \le 2, \\ 1, & x > 2. \end{cases}$$

A sketch of the c.d.f. is shown in Figure 4.1 (overleaf).

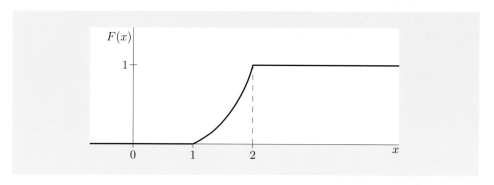

Figure 4.1   The c.d.f. of X

The c.d.f. can be used to calculate probabilities. For example,

$$P(X \le 1.5) = F(1.5)$$
$$= \tfrac{1}{3}(1.5^2 - 1)$$
$$\simeq 0.417,$$

$$P(X > 1.4) = 1 - P(X \le 1.4)$$
$$= 1 - F(1.4)$$
$$= 1 - \tfrac{1}{3}(1.4^2 - 1)$$
$$= 0.68,$$

$$P(1.2 < X \le 1.5) = P(X \le 1.5) - P(X \le 1.2)$$
$$= F(1.5) - F(1.2)$$
$$= \tfrac{1}{3}(1.5^2 - 1) - \tfrac{1}{3}(1.2^2 - 1)$$
$$= 0.27. \quad \blacklozenge$$

Activity 4.1   Oil changes

The time that it takes to complete an oil change in a car is between two and ten minutes. This time may be modelled by a random variable T with the c.d.f.

$$F(t) = \begin{cases} 0, & t < 2, \\ \dfrac{t^2 - 4}{96}, & 2 \le t \le 10, \\ 1, & t > 10. \end{cases}$$

(a) Calculate the probability that an oil change takes six minutes or less.

(b) Find the value of c if the probability that an oil change is completed in c minutes or less is equal to 0.9.

(c) Give a rough sketch of the c.d.f. of T.

Note that in Activity 4.1, the c.d.f. was defined for all $t \in \mathbb{R}$. This is formally correct, but when there is no fear of confusion, the statement '$F(t) = 0$ for $t < a$' is often omitted. For example, when the random variable T is time and $a = 0$, the statement is usually omitted. For clarity, in this section, the c.d.f. is defined for all real values in several of the examples.

The c.d.f. in Activity 4.1 is a continuous function of t, and this actually provides a mathematical definition of a **continuous random variable**: it is a random variable whose c.d.f. is continuous.

In M343 it will be assumed that $F(x)$, the c.d.f. of X, is differentiable for all $x \in \mathbb{R}$ except possibly at a finite number of points. The derivative of $F(x)$, when it exists, is denoted by $f(x)$ and is called the **probability density function** (p.d.f.). Hence, when $F'(x)$ exists,

$$F'(x) = f(x)$$

and

$$F(x) = \int_{-\infty}^{x} f(u)\, du.$$

u is a dummy variable.

For each point where $F(x)$ has a sudden change in gradient, so that it is not differentiable, the value of $f(x)$ may be chosen at will: the value of $f(x)$ at such points does not affect any probability calculations, and convenience determines the choice. This is illustrated in Example 4.2 and Activity 4.2.

The main properties of the p.d.f. are stated in the following box.

Properties of probability density functions

The p.d.f. f of a continuous random variable X has the following properties.

◇ $f(x) \geq 0,\ x \in \mathbb{R}$.

◇ $P(a < X \leq b) = \int_{a}^{b} f(x)\, dx.$

◇ $\int_{-\infty}^{\infty} f(x)\, dx = 1.$

The first property says that a p.d.f. cannot be negative. The second property means that the probability that X takes a value between a and b is given by the area under the graph of the p.d.f. between a and b. This is illustrated in Figure 4.2.

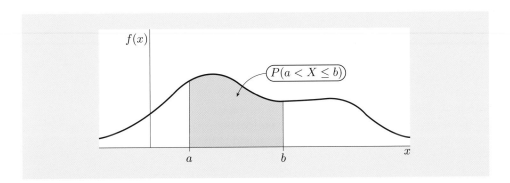

Figure 4.2   A probability density function

The shaded area in Figure 4.2 represents the probability $P(a < X \leq b)$. It also represents the probabilities $P(a \leq X \leq b)$, $P(a \leq X < b)$ and $P(a < X < b)$. Hence, for any continuous random variable X,

$$P(a \leq X \leq b) = P(a < X \leq b) = P(a \leq X < b) = P(a < X < b).$$

Note that although these probabilities are all equal for a continuous random variable, in general they are not equal if X is a discrete random variable. It is important to keep this difference in mind when calculating probabilities.

The third property of p.d.f.s says that the total area under the graph of the p.d.f. is equal to 1.

Example 4.2   A probability density function

For the random variable X whose c.d.f. $F(x)$ is given in Example 4.1, the p.d.f. can be found by differentiating the c.d.f. This gives

$$F'(x) = \begin{cases} 0, & x < 1, \\ \frac{2}{3}x, & 1 < x < 2, \\ 0, & x > 2. \end{cases}$$

The derivative cannot be calculated at $x = 1$ and $x = 2$. For convenience, f can be specified at $x = 1$ and $x = 2$ by $f(x) = \frac{2}{3}x$. So

$$f(x) = \begin{cases} \frac{2}{3}x, & 1 \le x \le 2, \\ 0, & \text{otherwise.} \end{cases}$$

In practice, the line '0 otherwise' is usually omitted, so that the p.d.f. is written simply as

$$f(x) = \tfrac{2}{3}x, \quad 1 \le x \le 2.$$

A sketch of the p.d.f. is shown in Figure 4.3(a).

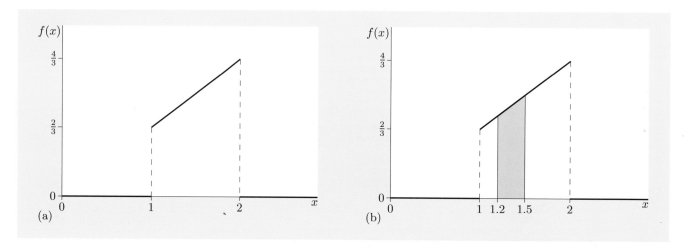

Figure 4.3   (a) The p.d.f. of X (b) The area representing $P(1.2 < X \le 1.5)$

The p.d.f. may be used to calculate probabilities by finding appropriate areas under its graph. For example, the probability $P(1.2 < X \le 1.5)$ is given by the area under the graph of the p.d.f. between $x = 1.2$ and $x = 1.5$, which is shaded in Figure 4.3(b).

Thus

$$\begin{aligned} P(1.2 < X \le 1.5) &= \int_{1.2}^{1.5} f(x)\,dx \\ &= \int_{1.2}^{1.5} \tfrac{2}{3}x\,dx \\ &= \left[\tfrac{1}{3}x^2\right]_{1.2}^{1.5} \\ &= \tfrac{1}{3}(1.5^2 - 1.2^2) \\ &= 0.27. \end{aligned}$$

This probability was obtained in Example 4.1 using the c.d.f. ◆

Activity 4.2   The p.d.f. of T

The random variable T, which represents the time it takes to complete an oil change in a car, was defined in Activity 4.1 by its c.d.f.

(a) Find $f(t)$, the p.d.f. of T.

(b) Use the p.d.f. to find the probability that an oil change takes more than six minutes but less than seven minutes.

(c) Sketch the p.d.f. of T.

To find the c.d.f. of a random variable from the p.d.f. involves integration. By definition,

$$F(x) = P(X \leq x).$$

This probability is found by calculating the area under the p.d.f. to the left of x, which is shaded in Figure 4.4:

$$F(x) = \int_{-\infty}^{x} f(u)\, du.$$

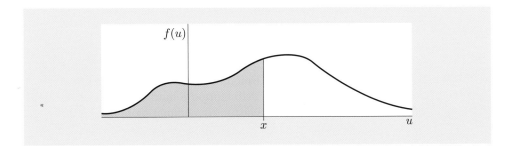

Figure 4.4   The shaded area is $P(X \leq x)$

Example 4.3   Finding the c.d.f. from the p.d.f.

Suppose that the p.d.f. of a random variable X is given by

$$f(x) = \tfrac{2}{3}x, \quad 1 \leq x \leq 2.$$

This is the p.d.f. obtained in Example 4.2; a sketch is given in Figure 4.3(a).

Clearly, since X can only take values between 1 and 2, $F(x) = 0$ for $x < 1$, and $F(x) = 1$ for $x > 2$. For $1 \leq x \leq 2$,

$$
\begin{aligned}
F(x) &= \int_{-\infty}^{x} f(u)\, du \\
&= \int_{-\infty}^{1} 0\, du + \int_{1}^{x} \tfrac{2}{3}u\, du \\
&= 0 + \left[\tfrac{1}{3}u^2\right]_{1}^{x} \\
&= \tfrac{1}{3}(x^2 - 1).
\end{aligned}
$$

$$\int_a^b f(x)\,dx = \Big[F(x)\Big]_a^b = F(b) - F(a)$$

where

Therefore

$$
F(x) = \begin{cases}
0, & x < 1, \\
\tfrac{1}{3}(x^2 - 1), & 1 \leq x \leq 2, \\
1, & x > 2.
\end{cases}
$$

This is the c.d.f. that was given in Example 4.1. ◆

Activity 4.3   Finding a c.d.f.

The p.d.f. of a random variable W is given by

$$f(w) = 2 - \tfrac{1}{2}w, \quad 2 \le w \le 4.$$

Find $F(w)$, the c.d.f. of W.

4.2 Expectation

The **expectation** of a continuous random variable X with p.d.f. $f(x)$ is defined analogously to that of a discrete variate, with an integral replacing the sum:

$$\mu = E(X) = \int_{-\infty}^{\infty} x\, f(x)\, dx.$$

Similarly, the expectation of a function $g(X)$ of a continuous random variable X is given by

$$E[g(X)] = \int_{-\infty}^{\infty} g(x)\, f(x)\, dx.$$

For example,

$$E(X^2) = \int_{-\infty}^{\infty} x^2\, f(x)\, dx.$$

The **variance** of X, $V(X)$, is defined by

$$V(X) = E[(X - \mu)^2] = \int_{-\infty}^{\infty} (x - \mu)^2 f(x)\, dx.$$

It is straightforward to show that, as in the discrete case,

$$V(X) = E(X^2) - \mu^2.$$

This formula is usually the easier to use of the two formulas for the variance. The above definitions are summarised in the following box.

Expectation for continuous random variables

For a continuous random variable X with p.d.f. $f(x)$, the **mean** or **expected value** or **expectation** of X, which is denoted by μ or $E(X)$, is given by

$$\mu = E(X) = \int_{-\infty}^{\infty} x\, f(x)\, dx. \tag{4.1}$$

The **expected value** of a function $g(X)$ of the random variable X is given by

$$E[g(X)] = \int_{-\infty}^{\infty} g(x)\, f(x)\, dx. \tag{4.2}$$

The **variance** of X, which is denoted by σ^2 or $V(X)$, is defined by

$$\sigma^2 = V(X) = E[(X - \mu)^2].$$

An alternative formula for the variance, which is often easier to use, is

$$\sigma^2 = V(X) = E(X^2) - \mu^2. \tag{4.3}$$

Example 4.4   Calculating the mean and variance

The p.d.f. of the random variable X of Examples 4.1, 4.2 and 4.3 is

$$f(x) = \tfrac{2}{3}x, \quad 1 \le x \le 2.$$

The mean, or expected value, of X is given by

$$\begin{aligned}
\mu = E(X) &= \int_{-\infty}^{\infty} x\, f(x)\, dx \\
&= \int_{1}^{2} x \times \tfrac{2}{3}x\, dx \\
&= \int_{1}^{2} \tfrac{2}{3}x^2\, dx \\
&= \left[\tfrac{2}{9}x^3\right]_{1}^{2} \\
&= \tfrac{16}{9} - \tfrac{2}{9} = \tfrac{14}{9} \simeq 1.556.
\end{aligned}$$

Similarly,

$$\begin{aligned}
E(X^2) &= \int_{-\infty}^{\infty} x^2\, f(x)\, dx \\
&= \int_{1}^{2} x^2 \times \tfrac{2}{3}x\, dx \\
&= \int_{1}^{2} \tfrac{2}{3}x^3\, dx \\
&= \left[\tfrac{1}{6}x^4\right]_{1}^{2} \\
&= \tfrac{16}{6} - \tfrac{1}{6} = 2.5.
\end{aligned}$$

Hence the variance of X is

$$\begin{aligned}
V(X) &= E(X^2) - \mu^2 \\
&= 2.5 - \left(\tfrac{14}{9}\right)^2 \\
&\simeq 0.080,
\end{aligned}$$

and the standard deviation of X is

$$\sqrt{V(X)} \simeq 0.283. \quad \blacklozenge$$

Activity 4.4   Calculating the mean and variance

Find the mean and variance of the random variable W whose p.d.f. was given in Activity 4.3.

Activity 4.5   Oil changes

Calculate the mean and variance of the time it takes to change the oil in a car, using the distribution in Activities 4.1 and 4.2.

An alternative formula for the mean

There is an alternative formula for the mean of a continuous random variable X that can take only non-negative values, which is analogous to Formula (2.4) for a discrete random variable. The formula is similar to Formula (2.4), but it contains an integral instead of a sum. It is stated without proof in the following box.

An alternative formula for the mean

For a continuous random variable X, whose range is a subset of $[0, \infty)$, the mean can be calculated using the formula

$$E(X) = \int_0^\infty (1 - F(x))\, dx. \qquad (4.4)$$

Note that for a continuous random variable X, the condition $P(X \geq 0) = 1$ is equivalent to the condition that the range of X is a subset of $[0, \infty)$.

This formula is particularly useful when finding the mean of a variate whose p.d.f. includes the exponential function, as you will see in Section 5. It could be applied to distributions such as the ones given in Example 4.1 and Activity 4.1, though the integration would not be made much simpler by doing so. Two examples of the use of the formula are given in Examples 4.5 and 4.6.

Example 4.5   Time to failure

The time to failure (in years) of a particular electrical component may be modelled by a random variable X with c.d.f. given by

$$F(x) = \tfrac{1}{4}x^2, \quad 0 \leq x \leq 2.$$

(Also $F(x) = 0$ for $x < 0$ and $F(x) = 1$ for $x > 2$.)

Since X cannot take negative values, the alternative formula for the mean (4.4) can be used to find the mean time to failure:

$$
\begin{aligned}
E(X) &= \int_0^\infty (1 - F(x))\, dx \\
&= \int_0^2 \left(1 - \tfrac{1}{4}x^2\right) dx + \int_2^\infty (1 - 1)\, dx \\
&= \left[x - \tfrac{1}{12}x^3\right]_0^2 + 0 \\
&= \tfrac{4}{3}.
\end{aligned}
$$

The mean time to failure is $\tfrac{4}{3}$ years or 16 months.   ◆

Example 4.6   Completing a task

A certain task always takes at least an hour to complete and sometimes takes much longer. The time T taken to complete the task may be modelled by a random variable T with c.d.f. given by

$$F(t) = 1 - \frac{1}{t^3}, \quad t \geq 1.$$

(Also $F(t) = 0$ for $t < 1$.)

Since T cannot take negative values, (4.4) can be used to find the mean time taken to complete the task.

The mean time is given by

$$
\begin{aligned}
E(T) &= \int_0^\infty (1 - F(t))\, dt \\
&= \int_0^1 (1 - 0)\, dt + \int_1^\infty \left(1 - \left(1 - \frac{1}{t^3}\right)\right) dt \\
&= \int_0^1 1\, dt + \int_1^\infty \frac{1}{t^3}\, dt \\
&= \left[t\right]_0^1 + \left[-\frac{1}{2t^2}\right]_1^\infty \\
&= 1 + \tfrac{1}{2} = 1\tfrac{1}{2}.
\end{aligned}
$$

So the mean time taken to complete the task is $1\tfrac{1}{2}$ hours. ◆

An important point to note from these examples is that the range of integration is always from 0 to ∞, whatever the range of the random variable. You need to remember that the c.d.f. is defined for all real values, not just for values in the range of the random variable. For instance, in Example 4.5, the fact that $F(x) = 1$ for $x > 2$ was used, and, in Example 4.6, the information that $F(t) = 0$ for $0 \le t < 1$ was used. Activities 4.6 and 4.7 will give you some practice at using the alternative formula (4.4).

Activity 4.6   The mean lifetime of birds

The length of life (in years) of a species of bird may be modelled by a random variable T with c.d.f.

$$
F(t) = 1 - \frac{1}{(t+1)^2}, \quad t \ge 0.
$$

Use Formula (4.4) to calculate the mean lifetime of birds of this species.

Activity 4.7   Oil changes

In Activity 4.1, the time in minutes taken to complete an oil change is modelled by a random variable T with c.d.f.

$$
F(t) = \frac{t^2 - 4}{96}, \quad 2 \le t \le 10.
$$

Note that $F(t) = 0$ for $t < 2$ and $F(t) = 1$ for $t > 10$.

Use Formula (4.4) to calculate the mean time taken to complete an oil change.

Sums of continuous random variables

The results described in Sections 2 and 3 for the expectation of sums of discrete random variables are also valid for sums of continuous random variables. For example, if $X_1, \ldots, X_n$ are continuous random variables, then

$$
E(X_1 + \cdots + X_n) = E(X_1) + \cdots + E(X_n). \tag{4.5}
$$

If, in addition, $X_1, \ldots, X_n$ are independent, then

$$
V(X_1 + \cdots + X_n) = V(X_1) + \cdots + V(X_n). \tag{4.6}
$$

Note that the continuous random variables $X_1, \ldots, X_n$ are independent if the occurrence of any event associated with any one of them is independent of the occurrence of any event associated with any of the others.

Independence for continuous random variables is discussed briefly in Subsection 7.2.

As was stated at the end of Section 3, many of the results obtained for the expectation of functions of discrete random variables also hold for continuous random variables. Such results will be used, when required, without proof.

Quantiles

For a continuous random variable X, the **median** is the value m that splits the probability distribution of X into two parts in such a way that $P(X \leq m) = \frac{1}{2}$ and $P(X \geq m) = \frac{1}{2}$. Equivalently, if $F(x)$ is the c.d.f. of X, then $F(m) = 1 - F(m) = \frac{1}{2}$. For a symmetric distribution, the area under the p.d.f. to the left of the mean is equal to $\frac{1}{2}$, so the median is equal to the mean.

In general, to find the median, the equation $F(m) = \frac{1}{2}$ must be solved for m. More generally, the solution of an equation of the form $F(x) = \alpha$, where $0 < \alpha < 1$, is called a **quantile**. The definition is given in the following box.

Quantiles for continuous distributions

For a continuous random variable X with c.d.f. $F(x)$, the **α-quantile** is the value x that is the solution of the equation

$$F(x) = \alpha, \quad 0 < \alpha < 1.$$

This value is denoted q_α.

That is, the α-quantile q_α satisfies $F(q_\alpha) = \alpha$ and is given by $q_\alpha = F^{-1}(\alpha)$, where F^{-1} is the inverse function of F.

The **median** is the value x that is the solution of the equation

$$F(x) = \tfrac{1}{2}.$$

That is, the median is $q_{0.5}$. It is usually denoted m.

It is assumed that F is strictly increasing for $x \in \Omega_X$. This is the case for all the continuous random variables that you will meet in M343.

Many statistical techniques depend on the idea of quantiles. For instance, in hypothesis testing, the 'extremes' or 'tails' of a distribution are important. So quantiles associated with values such as 0.9, 0.95, 0.99, at one extreme, and 0.1, 0.05, 0.01, at the other, are often used. And when exploring the properties of a proposed probability model, quantiles are often of interest. For example, when analysing a model for the service time of customers, the time within which 95% of customers are served might be found. Or when investigating a model for the lifetimes of individuals in a population, the age beyond which only 1% of the population live might be of interest.

Example 4.7   Finding quantiles

Suppose that a random variable X has c.d.f.

$$F(x) = x^4, \quad 0 \leq x \leq 1.$$

The median m satisfies $F(m) = \frac{1}{2}$, so

$$m^4 = \tfrac{1}{2},$$

and hence

$$m = 0.5^{1/4} \simeq 0.841.$$

The 0.95-quantile is the solution of $F(x) = 0.95$, so

$$F(q_{0.95}) = q_{0.95}^4 = 0.95,$$

and hence

$$q_{0.95} = 0.95^{1/4} \simeq 0.987. \quad \blacklozenge$$

Activity 4.8   Finding quantiles

Find the median m and the 0.99-quantile $q_{0.99}$ for the random variable X that has c.d.f.

$$F(x) = \tfrac{1}{9}x^2, \quad 0 \le x \le 3.$$

Summary of Section 4

In this section, the probability density function (p.d.f.) and the cumulative distribution function (c.d.f.) of a continuous random variable have been defined. You have learned how to obtain the p.d.f. from the c.d.f., and vice versa, and how to use these functions to calculate probabilities. You have seen that expectation for continuous variates is defined analogously to expectation for discrete variates, with sums being replaced by integrals. Formulas for the mean and variance have been given, including an alternative formula for the mean, which can be used when the range of the random variable is a subset of $[0, \infty)$. It has been noted that the results concerning sums of random variables discussed in Section 2 hold for continuous random variables as well as for discrete random variables. Quantiles for continuous random variables have been discussed briefly.

Exercises on Section 4

Exercise 4.1   *A continuous random variable*

The continuous random variable X has c.d.f.

$$F(x) = \tfrac{1}{4}x^2, \quad 0 \le x \le 2.$$

(a) Calculate $P(X < 0.4)$, $P(0.6 < X < 1.4)$ and $P(X > 1.6)$.

(b) Find the p.d.f. of X.

(c) Use the p.d.f. to calculate the mean and variance of X.

(d) Find the median of X.

(e) Find the value of $q_{0.9}$, the 0.9-quantile of X.

Exercise 4.2   *Another continuous random variable*

The continuous random variable X has p.d.f.

$$f(x) = \tfrac{1}{2}(x - 2), \quad 2 \le x \le 4.$$

(a) Calculate $P(X < 3)$.

(b) Use the p.d.f. to calculate the mean and variance of X.

(c) Find the c.d.f. of X.

(d) Use the alternative formula for the mean (4.4) to calculate the expected value of X.

(e) Find the median of X.

You will need to use the fact that the solutions of the quadratic equation $ax^2 + bx + c = 0$, where $a \ne 0$, are given by

$$x = \frac{-b \pm \sqrt{b^2 - 4ac}}{2a}.$$

5 Specific continuous distributions

In this section, the p.d.f.s of a number of common continuous distributions are given and some important properties of these distributions are described. You will have the opportunity to apply some of the techniques and results discussed in Section 4.

5.1 The continuous uniform distribution

The random variable X with p.d.f.

$$f(x) = \begin{cases} \dfrac{1}{b-a}, & a \le x \le b, \\ 0, & \text{otherwise}, \end{cases}$$

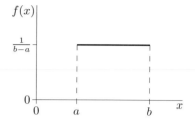

Figure 5.1 The p.d.f. of $X \sim U(a,b)$

is said to be **uniformly distributed** on the interval $[a, b]$. This is written $X \sim U(a, b)$. A sketch of the p.d.f. is shown in Figure 5.1. By symmetry, the mean of X is $\frac{1}{2}(a + b)$.

Activity 5.1 *The variance of $U(a, b)$*

Find the variance of the uniform distribution $U(a, b)$.

5.2 The exponential distribution

The random variable X with p.d.f.

$$f(x) = \lambda e^{-\lambda x}, \quad x \ge 0,$$

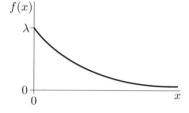

Figure 5.2 The p.d.f. of $X \sim M(\lambda)$

is said to have an **exponential distribution** with parameter λ. This is written $X \sim M(\lambda)$. A sketch of the p.d.f. is shown in Figure 5.2. The exponential distribution is used frequently in M343.

Activity 5.2 *The exponential distribution*

The random variable X has an exponential distribution with parameter λ.

(a) Obtain the c.d.f. of X.

(b) Find the mean of X using Formula (4.4).

(c) Find the variance of X. To do this, you will need to use integration by parts. Hence find the standard deviation of X.

The memoryless property

One of the most remarkable properties of the exponential distribution is known as the 'memoryless property'. Suppose, for example, that T, the duration of the time interval between cars passing a certain point, has an exponential distribution – that is, $T \sim M(\lambda)$. Then if an observer arrives at the point at any time, the time until the next car passes is also exponentially distributed with parameter λ. It is irrelevant how long an interval there has been with no car before the observer arrives. This property can be proved as follows.

Suppose that one car passes at time $t = 0$, and that by time c, when the observer arrives, no further car has passed. This implies that T, the interval between the first car passing and the next car passing, has duration greater than c. Let X be the time that the observer has to wait before a car passes him; then $T = c + X$. This situation is illustrated in Figure 5.3.

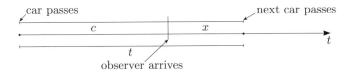

Figure 5.3   Cars passing a point

The probability that the observer has to wait longer than a time x is given by

$$P(X > x) = P(T > x + c \,|\, T > c)$$
$$= \frac{P([T > x + c] \cap [T > c])}{P(T > c)}$$

The definition of conditional probability has been used here.

$$= \frac{P(T > x + c)}{P(T > c)}$$
$$= \frac{1 - P(T \leq x + c)}{1 - P(T \leq c)}$$
$$= \frac{e^{-\lambda(x+c)}}{e^{-\lambda c}}, \quad \text{since } 1 - F(t) = e^{-\lambda t},$$
$$= e^{-\lambda x}.$$

This is independent of c, so the distribution of X, the time to the next event after time c, has c.d.f.

$$F(x) = P(X \leq x) = 1 - e^{-\lambda x}.$$

Hence X has an exponential distribution with parameter λ; that is, $X \sim M(\lambda)$.

It can be shown that not only does the exponential distribution possess the memoryless property, but it is the only continuous distribution possessing this property.

The proof of this result has been omitted.

The minimum of independent exponential variates

Another useful result concerns the distribution of the minimum of several independent exponential variates. Suppose that $T_1, T_2, \ldots, T_n$ are n independent exponential variates with parameters $\lambda_1, \lambda_2, \ldots, \lambda_n$, and that T is the minimum of $T_1, T_2, \ldots, T_n$. Since T is the minimum of $T_1, T_2, \ldots, T_n$, it follows that $T > t$ if and only if $T_1 > t, T_2 > t, \ldots, T_n > t$. Hence $[T > t]$ is the multiple event

$$[T_1 > t] \cap [T_2 > t] \cap \cdots \cap [T_n > t].$$

Since the random variables $T_1, T_2, \ldots, T_n$ are independent, the occurrence of any event associated with any one of them is independent of the occurrence of any event associated with any of the others. It follows that

$$P(T > t) = P(T_1 > t) \times P(T_2 > t) \times \cdots \times P(T_n > t).$$

Since $T_i \sim M(\lambda_i)$, $P(T > t_i) = e^{-\lambda_i t}$, and hence

$$P(T > t) = e^{-\lambda_1 t} \times e^{-\lambda_2 t} \times \cdots \times e^{-\lambda_n t}$$
$$= e^{-(\lambda_1 + \lambda_2 + \cdots + \lambda_n)t}.$$

Therefore the c.d.f. of T is

$$F_T(t) = 1 - e^{-(\lambda_1 + \lambda_2 + \cdots + \lambda_n)t}.$$

This is the c.d.f. of an exponential distribution with parameter $\lambda_1 + \lambda_2 + \cdots + \lambda_n$, so $T \sim M(\lambda_1 + \lambda_2 + \cdots + \lambda_n)$.

Thus the following result has been established.

The minimum of independent exponential variates

If T is the minimum of n independent exponential variates with parameters $\lambda_1, \lambda_2, \ldots, \lambda_n$, then

$$T \sim M(\lambda_1 + \lambda_2 + \cdots + \lambda_n).$$

You will need to use this result and the memoryless property in Activity 5.3.

Activity 5.3   Waiting to buy a ticket

Suppose that you arrive at the ticket office of your local railway station to find that all three sales assistants are busy serving customers, but no one is waiting. From past experience, you know that the times that the assistants take to serve a customer have exponential distributions with means 1 minute, 1.5 minutes and 3 minutes.

(a) Find the distribution of T, the time that you will have to wait until one of the assistants is free to serve you.

(b) Calculate the probability that you will have to wait less than 20 seconds.

5.3   The gamma distribution

If $X_1, X_2, \ldots, X_n$ are independent identically distributed exponential variates, each with parameter λ, then their sum $Y = X_1 + X_2 + \cdots + X_n$ has a **gamma distribution** with parameters n and λ. This is written $Y \sim \Gamma(n, \lambda)$. The p.d.f. of Y is

$$f(y) = \frac{y^{n-1}\lambda^n e^{-\lambda y}}{(n-1)!}, \quad y \geq 0.$$

Figure 5.4 shows the shape of the p.d.f. for $\lambda = 1$ and for several values of n.

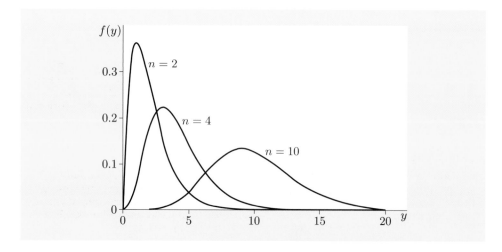

Figure 5.4   The p.d.f. of the gamma distribution $\Gamma(n, 1)$ for several values of n

If the duration of the interval between successive events has an exponential distribution, then the interval between an event and the nth event later is the sum of n independent identically distributed exponential variates, and hence has a gamma distribution.

In Activity 5.2, you found that the mean and variance of an exponential variate are $1/\lambda$ and $1/\lambda^2$, respectively. A gamma variate is the sum of n independent exponential variates, so using (4.5) and (4.6), it has mean n/λ and variance n/λ^2.

These results are given in Table 9 in the *Handbook*.

The expression for the c.d.f. of a gamma distribution can be obtained by repeated integration, but it has no simple form.

Activity 5.4   Queueing to buy a ticket

Suppose that you arrive at the ticket office of your local railway station to find that only one ticket window is open, the assistant is busy and two people are already waiting to be served. From past experience, you know that the service time of this assistant is exponentially distributed with mean 1.5 minutes.

(a) Write down the distribution of W, the time that you will have to wait until the assistant is free to serve you.

(b) Hence find the mean and standard deviation of your waiting time.

5.4   The normal distribution

The continuous random variable X with p.d.f.

$$f(x) = \frac{1}{\sigma\sqrt{2\pi}} \exp\left(-\frac{(x-\mu)^2}{2\sigma^2}\right), \quad x \in \mathbb{R},$$

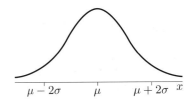

is said to have a **normal distribution** with mean μ and variance σ^2; this is written $X \sim N(\mu, \sigma^2)$. A sketch of this p.d.f. is shown in Figure 5.5. The normal distribution is very useful, especially in statistics, as it provides a good approximate model for the variability observed in many quantities.

Figure 5.5   The p.d.f. of $X \sim N(\mu, \sigma^2)$

If $X \sim N(\mu, \sigma^2)$, then the random variable $Z = (X - \mu)/\sigma$ is also normally distributed and has mean 0 and variance 1. This distribution is called the **standard normal distribution**, written $N(0, 1)$. Its p.d.f. is traditionally denoted by $\phi(z)$, where

$$\phi(z) = \frac{1}{\sqrt{2\pi}} e^{-z^2/2}, \quad z \in \mathbb{R}.$$

The c.d.f. of Z is denoted $\Phi(z)$:

$$\Phi(z) = \int_{-\infty}^{z} \frac{1}{\sqrt{2\pi}} e^{-u^2/2} \, du.$$

ϕ is the Greek lower-case letter phi, and Φ is the Greek upper-case letter phi. Both are pronounced 'fye'.

Since $Z = (X - \mu)/\sigma$, probabilities of events connected with the variate $X \sim N(\mu, \sigma^2)$ can be obtained from tables of $\Phi(z)$. A table of values of $\Phi(z)$, the c.d.f. of the standard normal distribution, is given in the *Handbook* (Table 1), together with a table of quantiles for $N(0, 1)$ (Table 2). The use of these tables is illustrated in Example 5.1.

Probabilities for normal distributions are available in many standard computer applications and on some calculators.

Example 5.1   Using tables for the standard normal distribution

The weights of packets of crisps labelled as containing 100 grams may be modelled by a normal distribution with mean 102 grams and standard deviation 1.6 grams. If W is the weight of a randomly selected packet, then $W \sim N(102, 1.6^2)$.

The probability that a randomly selected packet weighs less than 100 grams is

$$P(W < 100) = P\left(Z < \frac{100 - 102}{1.6}\right)$$
$$= \Phi(-1.25)$$
$$= 1 - \Phi(1.25)$$
$$= 1 - 0.8944$$
$$= 0.1056.$$

The standard normal distribution is symmetric about 0, so
$$P(Z \leq -z) = P(Z \geq z),$$
and hence
$$\Phi(-z) = 1 - \Phi(z).$$

If 99% of packets weigh less than w grams, then

$$P(W < w) = 0.99.$$

Equivalently,

$$P\left(Z < \frac{w - 102}{1.6}\right) = 0.99.$$

From Table 2 in the *Handbook*, $P(Z \leq 2.326) = 0.99$, so

$$\frac{w - 102}{1.6} = 2.326.$$

Hence

$$w = 102 + 1.6 \times 2.326 \simeq 105.7 \text{ grams.}$$

Therefore 99% of packets weigh less than approximately 105.7 grams. ◆

Activity 5.5   Using tables

Suppose that $X \sim N(16, 5)$.

(a) Calculate the probability that X lies between 15 and 18.

(b) Determine the value of c if $P(X > c) = 0.1$.

The normal distribution is also used to approximate the distribution of a sum of n independent identically distributed random variables. This approximation, which is good when n is large, is a consequence of an important result known as the central limit theorem. The theorem is stated in the following box.

The central limit theorem

If $X_1, X_2, \ldots, X_n$ are n independent identically distributed random variables with mean μ and variance σ^2, then for large n the distribution of their mean $\overline{X}$ is approximately normal with mean μ and variance σ^2/n:

$$\overline{X} \approx N\left(\mu, \frac{\sigma^2}{n}\right).$$

Equivalently, for large n, the distribution of their sum T is approximately normal with mean $n\mu$ and variance $n\sigma^2$:

$$T = X_1 + X_2 + \cdots + X_n \approx N(n\mu, n\sigma^2).$$

Activity 5.6   Using the central limit theorem

Suppose that $X_1, X_2, \ldots, X_{90}$ are independent identically distributed random variables with mean 2 and variance 3.

(a) What is the approximate distribution of $\overline{X}$, the mean of $X_1, X_2, \ldots, X_{90}$?

(b) Write down the approximate distribution of $T = X_1 + X_2 + \cdots + X_{90}$.

(c) Obtain an approximate value for the probability that the sum of the random variables takes a value greater than 200.

5.5   The χ^2 distribution

The distribution of the square of a standard normal variate is known as the **chi-squared distribution with one degree of freedom** and is denoted $\chi^2(1)$. In general, if $Z_1, Z_2, \ldots, Z_n$ are independent standard normal variates, then $W_n = Z_1^2 + Z_2^2 + \cdots + Z_n^2$ has the **chi-squared distribution with n degrees of freedom**, denoted $\chi^2(n)$. The p.d.f. of a $\chi^2(n)$ variate has quite a complicated form and is not needed for M343. However, you can get an idea of how the shape of the p.d.f. changes as n increases from the sketch in Figure 5.6, which shows the p.d.f. for four values of n.

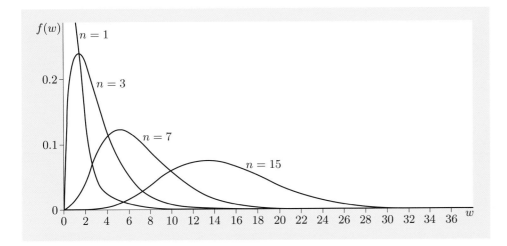

Figure 5.6   The p.d.f. of the chi-squared distribution $\chi^2(n)$ for $n = 1, 3, 7, 15$

Selected quantiles of the chi-squared distribution for different values of n are given in Table 3 in the *Handbook*. You will need to use this table in *Book 2*. If you are unsure how to use it, then try Activity 5.7.

Activity 5.7   Quantiles for chi-squared distributions

Use Table 3 in the *Handbook* to find the following quantiles.

(a) The 0.01-quantile and the 0.95-quantile of $\chi^2(5)$

(b) The 0.005-quantile and the 0.975-quantile of $\chi^2(10)$

(c) The 0.05-quantile and the 0.995-quantile of $\chi^2(23)$

The main properties of all the distributions described in this section are summarised in the table of continuous probability distributions in the *Handbook* (Table 9). You may quote results from this table whenever they are required.

Summary of Section 5

In this section, five families of continuous distributions have been described briefly: continuous uniform, exponential, gamma, normal and chi-squared. The exponential distribution is used widely in M343, so it has been discussed in some detail. The memoryless property of the exponential distribution has been proved, and the distribution of the minimum of independent exponential variates has been derived. You have also learned that a sum of independent identically distributed exponential variates has a gamma distribution. The normal distribution has been reviewed briefly, and the central limit theorem has been stated. The main properties of standard continuous distributions are summarised in Table 9 in the *Handbook*: the results in this table may be quoted without proof when required.

Exercises on Section 5

Exercise 5.1   Queueing in the supermarket

At my local supermarket there are two checkouts reserved for customers with baskets. Customers using these checkouts form a central queue. From past experience, it is known that the service times of the two assistants are exponentially distributed with means 2 minutes and 3 minutes.

Suppose that when I join the central queue, both assistants are busy, but no one else is waiting to be served.

(a) Find the distribution of the time that I will have to wait before one of the assistants is free. Calculate the probability that I will have to wait more than 2 minutes.

(b) Calculate the mean and standard deviation of the time that I will have to wait.

Exercise 5.2   Queueing at the checkout

One day, there is only one checkout open at my local supermarket for customers with baskets. The service time of the assistant is exponentially distributed with mean 2 minutes. When I join the queue, one person is being served, and two others are already waiting in the queue.

(a) Write down the distribution of the time that I will have to wait for my service to begin.

(b) Calculate the mean and standard deviation of my waiting time.

Exercise 5.3   Using the central limit theorem

Suppose that $X_1, X_2, \ldots, X_{160}$ are independent identically distributed random variables with mean 3 and variance 10.

(a) What is the approximate distribution of $\overline{X}$, the mean of $X_1, X_2, \ldots, X_{160}$?

(b) Write down the approximate distribution of $T = X_1 + X_2 + \cdots + X_{160}$.

(c) Obtain an approximate value for the probability that T takes a value less than 400.

6 Simulation

A major feature of M343 is the development of models for random phenomena. A useful method of investigating such models is simulation. The idea of simulation is to generate values in such a way that the results obtained are indistinguishable from those that might be observed if a physical experiment were actually carried out. Properties of the random variable or random phenomenon of interest can then be explored by inspecting the results. At various points in M343, you will use computer software to generate observations of random variables and random phenomena. The software uses a random number generator. In this section, tables of random numbers are used to illustrate how observations from a probability distribution can be simulated using random numbers. In Subsection 6.1, simulation for continuous distributions is discussed. Simulation for discrete distributions is described in Subsection 6.2.

6.1 Simulation for continuous distributions

The theorem stated in the following box is important because it leads directly to a straightforward method for simulating observations on any continuous random variable. Before explaining this method and giving some examples, a proof of the theorem will be given. You will not be expected to reproduce the proof; it is included for interest and completeness. In practice, you will be expected to use the result, not prove it.

The probability-integral transformation

If X is a continuous random variable with c.d.f. $F(x)$, then the variate $U = F(X)$ is uniformly distributed on $[0, 1]$.

First note that if $F(x)$ is a continuous increasing function, then it is one-to-one and its inverse function $F^{-1}(x)$ exists. Also, since $U = F(X)$ and F is the c.d.f. of X, U takes values between 0 and 1, that is, $0 \le U \le 1$. The c.d.f. of U is

$$\begin{aligned} F_U(u) &= P(U \le u) \\ &= P(F(X) \le u) \\ &= P(X \le F^{-1}(u)), \quad \text{since } F(x) \text{ is an increasing function,} \\ &= F(F^{-1}(u)) \\ &= u, \quad 0 \le u \le 1. \end{aligned}$$

By differentiation, $F_U'(u) = f_U(u) = 1$ for $0 \le u \le 1$, and hence $U \sim U(0, 1)$.

This result is used to simulate observations of a random variable X with c.d.f. $F(x)$ by solving the equation $F(x) = u$ for x, where u is an observation from $U(0, 1)$. This procedure is illustrated in Figure 6.1 and summarised in the following box.

This theorem holds even when $F(x)$ is constant over an interval of values of x. The proof requires a slight modification in this case.

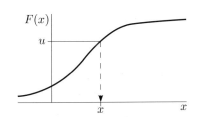

Figure 6.1 Simulation of a continuous random variable with c.d.f. $F(x)$ using an observation from $U(0, 1)$

Simulation for continuous distributions

If X is a continuous random variable with c.d.f. $F(x)$, then given a random observation u from $U(0, 1)$, an observation x from the distribution of X can be simulated by solving the equation $F(x) = u$.

Example 6.1   Simulating an observation

The random variable X of Example 4.1 has c.d.f.

$$F(x) = \begin{cases} 0, & x < 1, \\ \frac{1}{3}(x^2 - 1), & 1 \le x \le 2, \\ 1, & x > 2. \end{cases}$$

Given a random observation $u = 0.8165$ from $U(0,1)$, an observation from the distribution of X can be simulated by solving the equation $F(x) = u$:

$$\frac{1}{3}(x^2 - 1) = 0.8165.$$

Rearranging this gives

$$x^2 = 1 + 3 \times 0.8165.$$

So, taking the positive square root since $x > 0$,

$$x \simeq 1.857.$$

The simulated observation is 1.857.   ♦

Activity 6.1   Using the probability-integral transformation

(a) Find the c.d.f. of the random variable X with p.d.f.

$$f(x) = 4xe^{-2x^2}, \quad x \ge 0.$$

(b) Simulate an observation from the distribution of X using the number 0.4287, which is a random observation from $U(0,1)$.

A table of random digits is given in the *Handbook*. Part of this table is reproduced in Table 6.1.

Table 5 in the Handbook contains random digits.

Table 6.1   Random digits

74797	83014	65986	80571	52108
95448	70838	83516	39118	51251
24036	29038	43211	43902	38178
25727	64334	08691	18912	59396
40638	79467	53423	83490	35892

Each digit in the table was generated by a process that was equally likely to give any one of the ten digits $0, 1, \ldots, 9$. Random numbers from $U(0,1)$ can be formed from the digits in this table by taking groups of digits and placing a decimal point in front. For example, using groups of five digits, the top row would be read as $0.747\,97$, $0.830\,14$, and so on. Using the digits in this way, the table may be used together with the probability-integral transformation to simulate observations from any continuous probability distribution.

Activity 6.2   Lengths of telephone calls

The lengths of calls made by Abdul on his mobile phone are exponentially distributed with mean 5 minutes. Use the first four groups of digits from the bottom row of Table 6.1 to simulate the lengths of four telephone calls.

In Activity 6.2, you were asked to simulate observations from an exponential distribution with mean 5 minutes (parameter $\lambda = \frac{1}{5}$) by using observations from $U(0,1)$. Alternatively, a table of random numbers from $M(1)$, such as Table 6 in the *Handbook*, can be used. Part of that table is reproduced in Table 6.2.

Table 6.2　Random numbers from the exponential distribution with mean 1

1.2891	0.9435	1.0012	2.2380	0.0056
1.2566	1.2358	0.2606	1.9653	2.4839
0.5545	0.2233	0.5066	0.5960	1.4987
1.7001	0.3986	0.7155	2.8513	0.3744
1.1654	1.7995	0.0118	1.4248	0.4663

Simulated observations from $M(\lambda)$ are obtained by dividing these numbers by λ (or equivalently by multiplying them by the mean $1/\lambda$).

Activity 6.3　Simulating lengths of calls

Use the random numbers from the exponential distribution in Table 6.2 to simulate the lengths of four telephone calls made by Abdul on his mobile phone (see Activity 6.2). Use the first four numbers in the top row of the table.

The probability-integral transformation could also be used in conjunction with the table of probabilities for the standard normal distribution in the *Handbook* to simulate observations from a normal distribution. However, it is much simpler to use a table of random numbers from the standard normal distribution such as that in Table 7 in the *Handbook*, part of which is reproduced in Table 6.3.

Table 6.3　Random numbers from $N(0,1)$

−1.2968	0.1451	−0.6586	0.2838	0.4776
0.9502	−1.3210	−2.3439	1.2018	0.0094
0.6526	0.1518	0.2442	1.0086	−1.4396
0.3317	0.7231	0.3761	−1.4728	1.4707
−0.3612	−1.0574	−0.0405	−0.4928	0.3556

Observations from $N(\mu, \sigma^2)$ can be simulated by transforming the numbers in this table in the following way. Given a random number z from $N(0,1)$, the number

$$x = \sigma z + \mu$$

is a random observation from $N(\mu, \sigma^2)$.

Example 6.2　Foraging for food

An animal forages for food along a hedgerow in such a way that its distance (in metres) away from its burrow an hour after leaving it may be modelled by a random variable X with a normal distribution: $X \sim N(20, 100)$.

The random numbers from $N(0,1)$ in Table 6.3 can be used to simulate the animal's position an hour into a foraging expedition. For instance, using the numbers in the top row of the table, its distance from the burrow on each of three occasions may be found as follows.

Since $\mu = 20$ and $\sigma = \sqrt{100} = 10$, for each number z from the table, the simulated distance (in metres) is $x = 10z + 20$. So the three simulated distances are

$$x_1 = 10 \times -1.2968 + 20 \simeq 7.0 \text{ metres},$$
$$x_2 = 10 \times 0.1451 + 20 \simeq 21.5 \text{ metres},$$
$$x_3 = 10 \times -0.6586 + 20 \simeq 13.4 \text{ metres}. \quad \blacklozenge$$

Activity 6.4   Simulating observations from a normal distribution

Use the first three numbers in the final column of Table 6.3 to simulate three observations from the normal distribution $N(4, 9)$.

6.2   Simulation for discrete distributions

The main feature of any simulation scheme for a discrete distribution, based on a table of random digits, is that digits (or groups of digits) must be allocated to outcomes in such a way that the probability of any particular outcome occurring in the simulation is equal to the probability of that outcome in the distribution. For some discrete distributions, it is possible to construct a simulation scheme using single digits or pairs of digits instead of complete groups of digits from Table 5 in the *Handbook*. Very frequently, such a scheme will be simpler than one using more digits. An example of a scheme of this type is given in Example 6.3. Then a general method is described that uses groups of digits; this method is analogous to that used in Subsection 6.1 for continuous distributions.

Example 6.3   Simulating tosses of a coin

Tosses of a fair coin may be simulated using single random digits by allocating digits to outcomes according to the following scheme.

Digit	Outcome
0, 1, 2, 3, 4	Head
5, 6, 7, 8, 9	Tail

In this scheme, the same number of digits is allocated to a head (h) as to a tail (t), so the two outcomes are equally likely to occur. Using digits from the thirtieth row of the table of random digits in the *Handbook* to simulate the outcomes of ten tosses of the coin gives the following results.

Table 5 in the *Handbook* contains random digits.

Digit	2	3	8	6	1	8	9	2	4	2
Outcome	h	h	t	t	h	t	t	h	h	h

The simulation has resulted in six heads and four tails in ten tosses of the coin. $\blacklozenge$

Activity 6.5   Simulating the outcome of a game

(a) Describe a scheme using single random digits for simulating the outcomes of a series of games between two children, Alan and Barbara, in which the probability that Alan wins each game is $\frac{2}{3}$.

(b) Use digits from the fifth row of the table of random digits in the *Handbook* to simulate the outcomes of eight games between the two children.

Activity 6.6   Another simulation scheme

Describe a scheme using pairs of random digits for simulating the outcomes of the series of games in Activity 6.5 if the probability that Alan wins each game is 0.65. (You do not need to carry out a simulation.)

In Example 6.3, the outcomes of ten tosses of a fair coin were simulated. In doing so, the number of heads obtained in a sequence of ten tosses was also simulated (six in that simulation); that is, an observation from the binomial distribution $B\left(10, \frac{1}{2}\right)$ was simulated. Similarly, in Activity 6.5 an observation from the binomial distribution $B\left(8, \frac{2}{3}\right)$ was simulated. A similar method could be used to simulate observations from any binomial distribution, but in practice it could turn out to be a tedious exercise. Consider, for example, what would be involved in simulating six observations from the binomial distribution $B(50, 0.37)$. To obtain each simulated value, fifty observations from the Bernoulli distribution $B(1, 0.37)$ would need to be simulated and the number of successes counted. For six observations, this process would have to be repeated six times. Clearly, another method is required.

There is a general method for simulating observations from a discrete distribution that is analogous to that used for continuous distributions in Subsection 6.1. This method is illustrated in Figure 6.2.

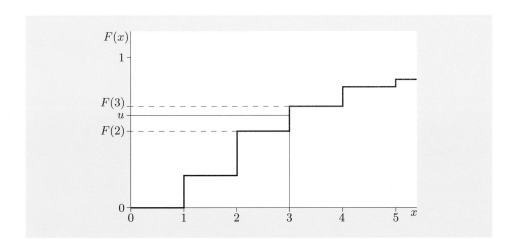

Figure 6.2   Simulation of a discrete random variable X using a value u from $U(0, 1)$

Note that if X is a discrete random variable, its c.d.f. $F(x)$ is a step function. In Figure 6.2, a horizontal line drawn at height u meets the c.d.f. at $x = 3$, so the simulated value of X, given the value u from $U(0, 1)$, is $x = 3$. In fact, for any value u such that $F(2) < u \leq F(3)$, the value u will give rise to a simulated value $x = 3$.

In general, given an observed value u from $U(0,1)$, the simulation procedure involves choosing x to satisfy

$$F(x-1) < u \leq F(x).$$

Then x is the simulated value corresponding to the observed value u from $U(0,1)$.

The procedure is summarised in the following box and illustrated in Example 6.4.

Simulation for discrete distributions

If X is a discrete integer-valued random variable with c.d.f. $F(x)$, then given a random observation u from $U(0,1)$, an observation x from the distribution of X can be simulated by choosing x to satisfy

$$F(x-1) < u \leq F(x).$$

Example 6.4   Using groups of digits

The random numbers $u_1 = 0.485\,79$, $u_2 = 0.743\,46$, $u_3 = 0.830\,42$ will be used to simulate three observations from the binomial distribution $B(8, 0.3)$.

These numbers were obtained using groups of digits from the seventh row of Table 5 in the *Handbook*.

To simulate observations, values of the c.d.f. must first be calculated. These are obtained by summing values of the p.m.f. Values of the p.m.f. and the c.d.f. are given in Table 6.4.

Table 6.4   The p.m.f. and c.d.f. of $B(8, 0.3)$

x	0	1	2	3	4	$\cdots$
$p(x)$	0.0576	0.1977	0.2965	0.2541	0.1361	$\cdots$
$F(x)$	0.0576	0.2553	0.5518	0.8059	0.9420	$\cdots$

Since

$$F(1) < 0.485\,79 \leq F(2),$$

the first simulated value of X is $x_1 = 2$. Similarly, since

$$F(2) < 0.743\,46 \leq F(3),$$

the second simulated value of X is $x_2 = 3$. The third simulated value is $x_3 = 4$, since $F(3) < 0.830\,42 \leq F(4)$.   ◆

Activity 6.7   Simulating observations from a Poisson distribution

Use the numbers in the twenty-sixth row of the table of random digits in the *Handbook* (beginning 09240) to simulate five observations from a Poisson distribution with mean 3.8.

See Table 5 in the *Handbook*.

Summary of Section 6

In this section, simulation has been discussed for both continuous and discrete distributions. You have learned how to use a table of random digits to simulate observations from a continuous distribution using the probability-integral transformation, and from a discrete distribution using an analogous method. In simple situations, you have derived simulation schemes that use single digits or pairs of digits.

Exercises on Section 6

Exercise 6.1 Simulating observations from a continuous distribution

Use numbers from the sixteenth row of the table of random digits in the *Handbook* to simulate three observations from a distribution with c.d.f.

$$F(x) = 1 - \frac{1}{x^3}, \quad x \geq 1.$$

Exercise 6.2 Simulating observations from an exponential distribution

The times in minutes between successive cars passing a cottage are exponentially distributed with mean 4. Simulate the times at which the first three cars pass the cottage after 9 am one morning using numbers from the fourth row of Table 6 in the *Handbook*.

Exercise 6.3 Simulating observations from a normal distribution

Use the numbers in the bottom row of the table of random numbers from $N(0,1)$ in the *Handbook* to simulate three observations from the normal distribution $N(6, 25)$.

Exercise 6.4 Simulating births

Of the babies born in a particular hospital, the proportion that are boys is 0.52.

(a) Devise a scheme that uses pairs of random digits for simulating the gender of babies born in the hospital.

(b) Use your scheme to simulate the gender of each of five babies born in the hospital. Use digits from the twentieth row of the table of random digits in the *Handbook*.

Exercise 6.5 Simulating observations from discrete distributions

(a) Use the number $u = 0.7423$, which is a random observation from $U(0, 1)$, to simulate an observation from the binomial distribution $B(9, 0.3)$.

(b) Use the number $u = 0.3817$, which is a random observation from $U(0, 1)$, to simulate an observation from the Poisson distribution with mean 2.5.

7 *Related variables*

Some of the ideas concerning relationships between two or more variables that have been introduced in earlier sections are brought together and extended in this section. In Subsection 7.1, the joint distribution of two discrete random variables is discussed, the idea of independence of such random variables is explored and the notion of a conditional distribution is introduced. Conditional expectation is also defined. In Subsection 7.2, these ideas are extended to continuous random variables. The Theorem of Total Probability is revisited in Subsection 7.3. Alternative forms of the theorem involving discrete and continuous random variables are discussed briefly, and some results for expectation that can be deduced from them are given.

The material in this section will not be assessed directly. However, many of the ideas and formulas are required in order to derive some of the results in *Books 2* to *5*, so you need to be familiar with them. We recommend that you work through this section now, then refer to it when necessary.

7.1 Discrete bivariate distributions

Ideas concerning the distribution of two related discrete random variables are discussed in this subsection. The examples used have been kept very simple so that the main ideas will not be obscured by the need for complicated calculations.

Joint and marginal distributions

The **joint probability mass function** for two discrete random variables X and Y, denoted $p(x, y)$, is defined by

$$p(x, y) = P(X = x, Y = y), \quad x \in \Omega_X, \ y \in \Omega_Y.$$

The use of $p(x, y)$ to denote $P(X = x, Y = y)$ was introduced in Subsection 2.1.

The distribution of X alone may be obtained by summing the joint p.m.f. over all possible values of y to give the p.m.f. of X. Similarly, the distribution of Y is obtained by summing the joint p.m.f. over all values of x. This is illustrated in Example 7.1.

Example 7.1 Keeping in touch

For the last few years, Mary has kept in touch with three friends by email. She has noticed that she never hears from more than two of them in any week. Frequently, she receives only one email and sometimes none at all. She doesn't email her friends every week, but when she does, she sends emails to all three of them. Let X represent the number of emails that she sends to her friends, and Y the number that she receives from them in a week. Suppose that the joint p.m.f. of X and Y is as shown in Table 7.1.

Table 7.1   The joint p.m.f. of X and Y

		y	
		0	1	2
x	0	0.1	0.4	0.1
	3	0	0.2	0.2

The entries in Table 7.1 are values of $p(x, y)$, the joint p.m.f. of X and Y. The p.m.f. of X is found by summing across the rows. For example,

$$P(X = 0) = P(X = 0, Y = 0) + P(X = 0, Y = 1) + P(X = 0, Y = 2),$$

that is,

$$p_X(0) = p(0, 0) + p(0, 1) + p(0, 2).$$

So

$$p_X(0) = 0.1 + 0.4 + 0.1 = 0.6.$$

Similarly,

$$p_X(3) = p(3, 0) + p(3, 1) + p(3, 2) = 0 + 0.2 + 0.2 = 0.4.$$

The p.m.f. of X is given in Table 7.2.

Table 7.2   The p.m.f. of X

x	0	3
$p_X(x)$	0.6	0.4

It follows that Mary does not send any emails to her friends in three weeks out of five (in a proportion 0.6 of weeks), and she sends emails to all three friends in two weeks out of five.

In a similar way, the p.m.f. of Y is obtained by summing down the columns:

$$p_Y(0) = p(0, 0) + p(3, 0) = 0.1,$$
$$p_Y(1) = p(0, 1) + p(3, 1) = 0.6,$$
$$p_Y(2) = p(0, 2) + p(3, 2) = 0.3.$$

The p.m.f. of Y is given in Table 7.3. This is the distribution of the number of emails that Mary receives from her friends in a week.

Note that for each $x \in \Omega_X$,

$$p_X(x) = \sum_{y \in \Omega_Y} p(x, y),$$

Table 7.3   The p.m.f. of Y

y	0	1	2
$p_Y(y)$	0.1	0.6	0.3

and for each $y \in \Omega_Y$,

$$p_Y(y) = \sum_{x \in \Omega_X} p(x, y).$$

The probabilities $p_X(x)$ and $p_Y(y)$ may conveniently be written in the margins of the table for $p(x, y)$, as in Table 7.4.

Table 7.4 The distributions of X and Y

		y		
		0	1	2	$p_X(x)$
x	0	0.1	0.4	0.1	0.6
	3	0	0.2	0.2	0.4
$p_Y(y)$		0.1	0.6	0.3	

The distributions of X alone and of Y alone, when obtained from the joint distribution of X and Y, are often called the **marginal distributions** of X and Y. The word *marginal* is used because these distributions are given by the entries in the margins of the table of joint probabilities. (Notice that the sum of the entries in each marginal distribution is 1.) The rule for finding the marginal distributions from the joint distribution is summarised in the following box.

Marginal distributions

If the discrete random variables X and Y have joint p.m.f. $p(x, y)$, $x \in \Omega_X$, $y \in \Omega_Y$, then the marginal distribution of X and the marginal distribution of Y are given by the p.m.f.s

$$p_X(x) = \sum_{y \in \Omega_Y} p(x, y), \quad x \in \Omega_X,$$

$$p_Y(y) = \sum_{x \in \Omega_X} p(x, y), \quad y \in \Omega_Y.$$

Activity 7.1 Finding marginal distributions

The random variables X and Y have the joint p.m.f. given in Table 7.5.

Find the marginal distributions of X and Y.

Table 7.5 A joint p.m.f.

		y		
		0	1	2
x	1	0.1	0.2	0.2
	2	0.1	0.3	0.1

Conditional distributions

You have seen how the joint distribution of two discrete random variables can be represented by a joint p.m.f., and how to obtain the marginal distributions of the two random variables from the joint p.m.f. Now suppose that the value of one random variable is observed. What information does this provide about the value of the other random variable?

Example 7.2 If three emails are sent

For the situation in Example 7.1, suppose that Mary sends three emails one week. What is the probability that she receives one email that week?

To answer this, the conditional probability $P(Y = 1 \mid X = 3)$ is required. By the definition of conditional probability,

$$P(Y = 1 \mid X = 3) = \frac{P([Y = 1] \cap [X = 3])}{P(X = 3)} = \frac{p(3, 1)}{p_X(3)} = \frac{0.2}{0.4} = 0.5.$$

For events A and E,
$$P(A|E) = \frac{P(A \cap E)}{P(E)},$$
provided that $P(E) \neq 0$. (This is the definition given in (1.4).)

Similarly,

$$P(Y = 0 \mid X = 3) = \frac{p(3,0)}{p_X(3)} = 0,$$

$$P(Y = 2 \mid X = 3) = \frac{p(3,2)}{p_X(3)} = \frac{0.2}{0.4} = 0.5.$$

So the distribution of the number of emails that Mary receives (Y) given that she sends three $(X = 3)$ is as follows.

y	0	1	2
$P(Y = y \mid X = 3)$	0	0.5	0.5

The notation $p(y|3)$ is used for this p.m.f. The distribution is called the **conditional distribution** of Y given $X = 3$. ◆

In general, the notation $p(y|x)$ is used for the p.m.f. of the conditional distribution of Y given $X = x$. Note that this distribution is a *univariate* distribution of the random variable Y for a fixed value x of X.

Activity 7.2   If no emails are sent

Find the conditional distribution of the number of emails that Mary receives in a week given that she does not send any emails that week. That is, find the p.m.f. $p(y|0)$.

The p.m.f. of the conditional distribution of X given $Y = y$ is defined similarly. It is denoted by $p(x|y)$ and, provided that $P(Y = y) \neq 0$,

$$p(x|y) = \frac{P([X = x] \cap [Y = y])}{P(Y = y)} = \frac{p(x,y)}{p_Y(y)}.$$

Activity 7.3   If one email is received

Find the conditional distribution of the number of emails that Mary sends in a week given that she receives one email. That is, find the probabilities $p(x|1)$ for $x = 0$ and $x = 3$.

The conditional distributions just described are defined formally in the following box.

Conditional distributions

Suppose that X and Y are discrete random variables with joint p.m.f. $p(x,y)$ and marginal distributions with p.m.f.s $p_X(x)$ and $p_Y(y)$, respectively. Then the p.m.f.s of the **conditional distributions** of Y given $X = x$ and of X given $Y = y$ are denoted $p(y|x)$ and $p(x|y)$, respectively, and are given by

$$p(y|x) = \frac{p(x,y)}{p_X(x)} \quad \text{if } p_X(x) > 0,$$

$$p(x|y) = \frac{p(x,y)}{p_Y(y)} \quad \text{if } p_Y(y) > 0.$$

Independence

In Subsection 2.1, two random variables were defined to be independent if the occurrence of any event associated with one of them does not depend on the occurrence of any event associated with the other. It follows that if X and Y are independent discrete random variables, then for all $y \in \Omega_Y$ and for all $x \in \Omega_X$,

$$P(X = x \mid Y = y) = P(X = x),$$

that is,

$$p(x|y) = p_X(x) \quad \text{for all } x \in \Omega_X, \ y \in \Omega_Y.$$

By definition,

$$p(x|y) = \frac{p(x, y)}{p_Y(y)}, \quad \text{provided that } p_Y(y) \neq 0.$$

Therefore, if X and Y are independent, then

$$p(x, y) = p_X(x) \, p_Y(y) \quad \text{for all } x \in \Omega_X, \ y \in \Omega_Y.$$

This is the condition for independence that was stated without proof in Subsection 2.1. It can be used to provide a formal definition of independence that is straightforward to use in practice.

Independent random variables

Two discrete random variables X and Y are **independent** if

$$p(x, y) = p_X(x) \, p_Y(y) \quad \text{for all } x \in \Omega_X, \ y \in \Omega_Y.$$

Example 7.3 *Writing and receiving emails*

The joint distribution of the number of emails that Mary receives and the number that she sends in a week, and the marginal distributions, which were given in Table 7.4, are repeated in Table 7.6.

Since $p(0, 0) = 0.1$ and $p_X(0) \, p_Y(0) = 0.6 \times 0.1 = 0.06$,

$$p(0, 0) \neq p_X(0) \, p_Y(0).$$

Therefore X and Y are not independent. ◆

Table 7.6 Joint and marginal distributions

		y			
		0	1	2	$p_X(x)$
x	0	0.1	0.4	0.1	0.6
	3	0	0.2	0.2	0.4
$p_Y(y)$		0.1	0.6	0.3	

Note that to show that two random variables are *not* independent, it is only necessary to find *one* pair of values x, y for which $p(x, y) \neq p_X(x) \, p_Y(y)$. However, to show that two random variables *are* independent, you must show that $p(x, y) = p_X(x) \, p_Y(y)$ for *all* $x \in \Omega_X, y \in \Omega_Y$. This is illustrated in Example 7.4.

Example 7.4 *Independence*

The joint p.m.f. of two discrete random variables X and Y is given in Table 7.7, together with the marginal distributions of X and Y.

Notice that

$$p_X(0) \, p_Y(0) = 0.8 \times 0.25 = 0.2 = p(0, 0),$$
$$p_X(1) \, p_Y(0) = 0.2 \times 0.25 = 0.05 = p(1, 0),$$

and so on. In fact, for $x = 0, 1$ and $y = 0, 1, 2$,

$$p(x, y) = p_X(x) \, p_Y(y).$$

Therefore X and Y are independent. ◆

Table 7.7 Joint and marginal distributions

		y			
		0	1	2	$p_X(x)$
x	0	0.2	0.4	0.2	0.8
	1	0.05	0.1	0.05	0.2
$p_Y(y)$		0.25	0.5	0.25	

Activity 7.4 *Independent or not?*

For each of the following joint p.m.f.s, decide whether or not X and Y are independent.

(a)

		y	
		0	1
x	0	0.3	0.2
	1	0.3	0.2

(b)

		y	
		0	1
x	0	0.2	0.3
	1	0.4	0.1

(c)

		y	
		0	1
x	0	0.45	0.3
	1	0.15	0.1

Conditional expectation

As already noted, the conditional distribution of a random variable Y given $X = x$ is a univariate distribution. It follows that for each value x, the distribution has a mean or expectation. The mean of the conditional distribution of Y given $X = x$, which is denoted $E(Y \mid X = x)$, is called the **conditional expectation** of Y given $X = x$. For discrete random variables X and Y,

$$E(Y \mid X = x) = \sum_{y \in \Omega_Y} y\, P(Y = y \mid X = x) = \sum_{y \in \Omega_Y} y\, p(y|x).$$

Example 7.5 *Conditional expectation*

The mean number of emails that Mary receives in a week when she sends three emails is given by the mean of the conditional distribution of Y given $X = 3$, that is, by $E(Y \mid X = 3)$. The conditional p.m.f. $p(y|3)$, which was found in Example 7.2, is repeated in Table 7.8.

Table 7.8 A conditional p.m.f.

y	0	1	2
$p(y|3)$	0	0.5	0.5

Therefore

$$E(Y \mid X = 3) = 0 \times 0 + 1 \times 0.5 + 2 \times 0.5 = 1.5. \quad \blacklozenge$$

Similarly, the conditional expectation of X given $Y = y$ is defined to be the mean of the conditional distribution of X given $Y = y$. Thus, if X and Y are discrete, then

$$E(X \mid Y = y) = \sum_{x \in \Omega_X} x\, P(X = x \mid Y = y) = \sum_{x \in \Omega_X} x\, p(x|y).$$

Activity 7.5 *Conditional expectations*

For the email-sending and email-receiving situation of Example 7.1, answer the following questions.

(a) Calculate the mean number of emails that Mary receives in a week when she does not send any emails.

(b) Calculate the mean number of emails that Mary sends in a week when she receives one email.

You will need to use your answers to Activities 7.2 and 7.3.

Activity 7.6 should help you to familiarise yourself with some of the ideas introduced in this subsection.

Activity 7.6   *Marginal distributions and conditional expectation*

The joint p.m.f. of two discrete random variables X and Y is given in Table 7.9.

Table 7.9   A joint p.m.f.

		y		
		0	1	2
x	1	0.05	0.2	0.1
	2	0.2	0.15	0.3

(a)   Find the marginal distributions of X and Y.

(b)   Calculate the expectations $E(Y \mid X = 1)$ and $E(X \mid Y = 2)$.

7.2   Continuous bivariate distributions

A summary of basic ideas concerning continuous bivariate distributions is given in this subsection. The ideas are similar to those just discussed for discrete random variables, and the results given are analogous to those for discrete random variables.

Joint and marginal distributions

The joint distribution of two discrete random variables X and Y is defined by the joint p.m.f. $p(x, y)$. Correspondingly, the joint distribution of two continuous random variables is defined by a **joint probability density function**.

In Subsection 4.1, you saw that a p.d.f. is a function $f(x)$ with the following properties:

◇ $f(x) \geq 0$, $x \in \mathbb{R}$.

◇ $P(a < X \leq b) = \displaystyle\int_a^b f(x)\,dx$.

◇ $\displaystyle\int_{-\infty}^{\infty} f(x)\,dx = 1$.

The distribution of a random variable X is completely determined by the p.d.f.

The graph of a p.d.f. $f(x)$ is a curve in two dimensions. The first property states that the graph of the p.d.f. always lies on or above the x-axis. The second property describes how the p.d.f. is used to calculate probabilities: they are given by areas between the p.d.f. and the x-axis. This is illustrated in Figure 7.1. The third property states that the total area between the p.d.f. and the x-axis is equal to 1.

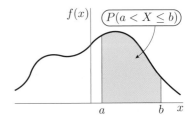

Figure 7.1   A p.d.f.: the shaded area gives $P(a < X \leq b)$

The joint distribution of two continuous random variables X and Y can be completely specified by a joint p.d.f. $f(x,y)$. The function $z = f(x,y)$ represents a surface in three dimensions, the height of the surface above the x-y plane at the point (x,y) being $z = f(x,y)$. If $f(x,y)$ is the joint p.d.f. of two continuous random variables, then volumes of regions between this surface and the x-y plane represent probabilities.

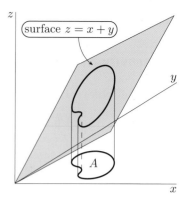

A joint p.d.f. $f(x,y)$ has the following three properties corresponding to the properties for a p.d.f. $f(x)$.

◇ $f(x,y) \geq 0$ for all x and y.

◇   The probability that the random variables X and Y take a pair of values (x,y) within a region A of the x-y plane is given by the volume contained between the surface $z = f(x,y)$ and the area A in the x-y plane. (This is illustrated in Figure 7.2 for $f(x,y) = x + y$.)

◇   The total volume contained between the surface $z = f(x,y)$ and the x-y plane is 1.

Figure 7.2   The volume shown gives the probability that X and Y take values (x,y) within A

For two discrete random variables, X and Y, with joint p.m.f. $p(x,y)$, the marginal distribution of X is found by summing $p(x,y)$ over all possible values of y, that is,

$$p_X(x) = \sum_{y \in \Omega_Y} p(x,y), \quad x \in \Omega_X.$$

In general, wherever a sum occurs with discrete random variables, an integral occurs for continuous distributions. If X and Y have joint p.d.f. $f(x,y)$, then $f_X(x)$, the **marginal p.d.f.** of X, is given by

$$f_X(x) = \int_{-\infty}^{\infty} f(x,y)\, dy, \quad -\infty < x < \infty.$$

Similarly, the **marginal p.d.f.** of Y is given by

$$f_Y(y) = \int_{-\infty}^{\infty} f(x,y)\, dx, \quad -\infty < y < \infty.$$

Example 7.6   Marginal distributions

The random variables X and Y have joint p.d.f.

$$f(x,y) = x + y, \quad 0 \leq x \leq 1,\ 0 \leq y \leq 1.$$

When integrating $f(x,y)$ with respect to y, x is treated as if it were a constant. So for $0 \leq x \leq 1$,

$$\begin{aligned}
f_X(x) = \int_{-\infty}^{\infty} f(x,y)\, dy &= \int_0^1 (x+y)\, dy \\
&= \left[xy + \tfrac{1}{2}y^2 \right]_0^1 \\
&= x + \tfrac{1}{2}. \quad \blacklozenge
\end{aligned}$$

Activity 7.7   Marginal distributions

If the random variables X and Y have the joint p.d.f. of Example 7.6, find the marginal p.d.f. of Y.

Conditional distributions, independence and conditional expectation

Given two continuous random variables X and Y, the p.d.f. of a conditional distribution is defined analogously to the p.m.f. of a conditional distribution involving two discrete random variables. The **conditional p.d.f.** of Y given $X = x$ is written $f(y|x)$. For any x such that $f_X(x) > 0$, it is given by

$$f(y|x) = \frac{f(x,y)}{f_X(x)}.$$

Similarly, for any y such that $f_Y(y) > 0$, the conditional p.d.f. of X given $Y = y$, written $f(x|y)$, is given by

$$f(x|y) = \frac{f(x,y)}{f_Y(y)}.$$

Thus the joint p.d.f., the marginal p.d.f.s and the conditional p.d.f.s satisfy

$$f(x,y) = f(x|y)\, f_Y(y) = f(y|x)\, f_X(x).$$

Continuing the analogy with discrete variates, the independence of two continuous random variables can be defined as in the following box.

Independent random variables

Two continuous random variables X and Y are said to be **independent** if

$$f(x,y) = f_X(x)\, f_Y(y) \quad \text{for all values of } x \text{ and } y.$$

The conditional expectation of Y given $X = x$, and the conditional expectation of X given $Y = y$, are defined analogously with conditional expectations for discrete random variables. Integration replaces summation, and p.d.f.s replace p.m.f.s. For continuous random variables X and Y, the conditional expectation of Y given $X = x$ is given by

$$E(Y \mid X = x) = \int_{-\infty}^{\infty} y\, f(y|x)\, dy.$$

Similarly, the conditional expectation of X given $Y = y$ is given by

$$E(X \mid Y = y) = \int_{-\infty}^{\infty} x\, f(x|y)\, dx.$$

Some familiarity with joint and conditional distributions for continuous random variables is required in order to follow the derivation of a result in *Book 5*. However, you will not be expected to apply any of the ideas from this subsection to solve problems.

7.3 The Theorem of Total Probability

The Theorem of Total Probability, as described in Subsection 1.3, gives an expression for the probability of occurrence of an event A when A occurs simultaneously with one of a set of mutually exclusive and exhaustive events $E_1, E_2, \ldots, E_n$:

$$P(A) = \sum_{i=1}^{n} P(A|E_i)\, P(E_i). \tag{7.1}$$

A form of the theorem involving an event A and a discrete random variable Y can be obtained by noting that Y must take one and only one value in its state space Ω_Y. Thus the events $[Y = y]$, $y \in \Omega_Y$, are mutually exclusive and exhaustive, and hence for any event A and any discrete random variable Y,

$$P(A) = \sum_{y \in \Omega_Y} P(A \mid Y = y)\, P(Y = y). \tag{7.2}$$

An analogous result for the situation where Y is a continuous random variable is obtained by replacing the p.m.f. $p_Y(y) = P(Y = y)$ by a p.d.f. and summation by integration: for any event A and any continuous random variable Y with p.d.f. $f_Y(y)$,

$$P(A) = \int_{-\infty}^{\infty} P(A \mid Y = y) f_Y(y) \, dy.$$

If X is a discrete random variable, then letting A be the event $[X = x]$ in (7.2) gives the Theorem of Total Probability in a form that applies to two discrete random variables:

$$P(X = x) = \sum_{y \in \Omega_Y} P(X = x \mid Y = y) P(Y = y), \tag{7.3}$$

or equivalently,

$$p_X(x) = \sum_{y \in \Omega_Y} p(x|y) \, p_Y(y). \tag{7.4}$$

An analogous result for two continuous random variables X and Y is obtained by replacing the p.m.f.s by p.d.f.s and summation by integration in (7.4):

$$f_X(x) = \int_{-\infty}^{\infty} f(x|y) f_Y(y) \, dy. \tag{7.5}$$

> The theorem is used in this form in *Book 5*.

Statements of the Theorem of Total Probability for one discrete and one continuous random variable are as follows.

If X is a continuous random variable and Y is a discrete random variable, then

$$f_X(x) = \sum_{y \in \Omega_Y} f(x \mid Y = y) P(Y = y). \tag{7.6}$$

> The theorem is used in this form in *Book 4*.

If X is a discrete random variable and Y is a continuous random variable, then

$$p_X(x) = P(X = x) = \int_{-\infty}^{\infty} P(X = x \mid Y = y) f_Y(y) \, dy. \tag{7.7}$$

Expectation

Results (7.4) to (7.7) can be used to obtain formulas for $E(X)$ in terms of the conditional expectations $E(X \mid Y = y)$, $y \in \Omega_Y$. For instance, suppose that X and Y are discrete random variables. By definition,

$$E(X) = \sum_{x \in \Omega_X} x \, p_X(x).$$

Using the Theorem of Total Probability as stated in (7.4) to substitute for $p_X(x)$ gives

$$E(X) = \sum_{x \in \Omega_X} x \sum_{y \in \Omega_Y} p(x|y) \, p_Y(y)$$

$$= \sum_{y \in \Omega_Y} \left(\sum_{x \in \Omega_X} x \, p(x|y) \right) p_Y(y)$$

$$= \sum_{y \in \Omega_Y} E(X \mid Y = y) \, p_Y(y).$$

> The order of the two summations has been changed here. You may assume that it is valid to do so.

That is, for discrete random variables X and Y,

$$E(X) = \sum_{y \in \Omega_Y} E(X \mid Y = y) P(Y = y). \tag{7.8}$$

> This result is used in *Books 2* and *3*.

In fact, the formula for $E(X)$ in (7.8) can also be used when X is continuous and Y is discrete. (For X continuous, (7.8) can be deduced from (7.6).)

The corresponding formula for the situation where Y is continuous and X is either discrete or continuous follows from (7.5) and (7.7):

$$E(X) = \int_{-\infty}^{\infty} E(X \mid Y = y) \, f_Y(y) \, dy.$$

All the results discussed in this subsection are in the *Handbook*.

Summary of Section 7

In this section, some ideas concerning relationships between two discrete random variables or between two continuous random variables have been introduced. In particular, conditional distributions and conditional expectation have been defined. The Theorem of Total Probability has been discussed, and the theorem has been stated in several forms in which the events involve random variables. Formulas for the mean of a random variable in terms of conditional expectations have been given.

Exercises on Section 7

Exercise 7.1   Conditional expectation

The random variables X and Y have the joint distribution specified by the following table.

		y		
		1	2	3
x	0	0.1	0.2	0.3
	1	0.2	0.1	0.1

(a) Complete the table to show the marginal distributions of the random variables X and Y.

(b) Calculate the expectation $E(Y \mid X = 1)$.

Exercise 7.2   Another conditional expectation

The random variables X and Y have the joint distribution specified by the following table.

		y		
		0	1	2
x	0	$\frac{1}{8}$	0	$\frac{1}{3}$
	1	$\frac{1}{6}$	$\frac{3}{8}$	0

(a) Complete the table to show the marginal distributions of the random variables X and Y.

(b) Calculate the expectation $E(X \mid Y = 0)$.

8 Useful mathematical results and techniques

This section contains a brief review of some of the mathematical results and techniques that you will need to use as you study M343. Rules for manipulating powers, logarithms and exponential functions are summarised in Subsection 8.1, and geometric series are discussed briefly in Subsection 8.2. Basic differentiation and integration are discussed in Subsection 8.3, and two methods for solving ordinary differential equations are described in Subsection 8.4.

If you are confident at applying the techniques described, then you will not need to study this section. Whether or not you work through any of the material is up to you. You may prefer simply to refer to it if you find that you need to revise some of the techniques described.

8.1 Powers, logarithms and exponential functions

Powers

If n is a positive integer and x is any real number, then x^n is notation for the nth power of x. That is, $x^n = x \times x \times \cdots \times x$, where this product contains n factors. The nth power of x is also defined when n is 0, negative or a rational number.

◇ $x^0 = 1$

◇ $x^{-n} = \dfrac{1}{x^n}$, $x \neq 0$

◇ $x^{1/n} = \sqrt[n]{x}$

◇ $x^{m/n} = \sqrt[n]{x^m} = \left(\sqrt[n]{x}\right)^m$

The following rules can be used to manipulate powers.

◇ $x^a \times x^b = x^{a+b}$

◇ $\left(x^a\right)^b = x^{ab}$

◇ $\dfrac{x^a}{x^b} = x^{a-b}$

Activity 8.1 Evaluating powers

Calculate the value of each of the following numbers.

(a) 3^2 (b) 2^{-3} (c) $27^{1/3}$ (d) $16^{3/4}$ (e) $25^{-1/2}$

Activity 8.2 Using the rules

Simplify each of the following expressions.

(a) $x^2 \times x^4$ (b) $\left(x^3\right)^2$ (c) x^8/x^2

Logarithms and exponentials

All the logarithms used in M343 are natural logarithms, that is, logarithms to base e. The logarithm to base e of x, where $x > 0$, is sometimes denoted $\log_e x$ or $\ln x$. However, the notation $\log x$ is used throughout M343. On many calculators, the key labelled 'ln' gives natural logarithms, and the key labelled 'log' gives logarithms to base 10. To check which button on your calculator gives natural logarithms, try using your calculator to find the natural logarithm of e (which is equal to 1).

$e \simeq 2.718\,28$

Logarithms can be manipulated using the following rules.

◇ $\log a + \log b = \log(ab)$, $a > 0$, $b > 0$

◇ $\log a - \log b = \log\left(\dfrac{a}{b}\right)$, $a > 0$, $b > 0$

◇ $\log(a^n) = n \log a$, $a > 0$

Note that $\log 1 = 0$.

The inverse of the natural logarithm function $x \longmapsto \log x$ is the exponential function $x \longmapsto \exp(x) = e^x$. Hence, for $x > 0$,

$$\log(\exp(x)) = \exp(\log x) = x,$$

or equivalently,

$$\log e^x = e^{\log x} = x.$$

Since e^x is a power, the rules for manipulating powers apply to exponentials.

◇ $e^a \times e^b = e^{a+b}$

◇ $(e^a)^b = e^{ab}$

◇ $\dfrac{e^a}{e^b} = e^{a-b}$

Activity 8.3   Logarithms and exponentials

(a) If $y = \log 6 + \log 4 - \log 3$, write y as a single logarithm.

(b) If $y = 2 \log x - 3 \log(x + 1)$, write y as a single logarithm.

(c) Use the rules for manipulating logarithms to find the value of $\log 8/\log 2$.

(d) Simplify $e^{4x} \times \left(e^{-3x}\right)^2$.

(e) If $y = \log s - \log(1 - s) - kt$, show that

$$e^y = \frac{s}{1 - s}\, e^{-kt}.$$

Activity 8.4   Inverse functions

Use the fact that the exponential function is the inverse of the natural logarithm function to write each of the following as expressions that do not involve logarithms and exponentials.

(a) $y = \log e^{3x}$

(b) $y = e^{\log(2x+3)}$

(c) $y = e^{4 \log((10-x)/10)}$

(d) $y = e^{-3 \log(1+x)}$

8.2   Geometric series

Each term in a geometric series is a constant multiple of the previous term. The following result for the sum of a geometric series is used on many occasions in M343 (including in Subsections 2.2 and 3.2 of this book).

The sum of a geometric series

For $-1 < x < 1$,

$$1 + x + x^2 + \cdots = \sum_{j=0}^{\infty} x^j = \frac{1}{1-x}.$$

This result can be used either to sum a geometric series or to expand a function of the form $1/(1-x)$ as a power series in x.

Example 8.1   Summing geometric series

First, consider the series $S_1 = q + qp + qp^2 + \cdots$. Each term in the series is p times the previous term, so it is a geometric series and, for $-1 < p < 1$,

$$S_1 = q(1 + p + p^2 + \cdots)$$
$$= q \times \frac{1}{1-p}$$
$$= \frac{q}{1-p}.$$

(Note that when $0 < p < 1$ and $q = 1 - p$, the terms in this series are the probabilities in the geometric distribution $G_0(p)$, and in this case $S_1 = 1$.)

Next, consider the series $S_2 = 4s^2 + 2s^3 + s^4 + \frac{1}{2}s^5 + \cdots$. Each term is equal to the previous term multiplied by $\frac{1}{2}s$, so the series is a geometric series and, for $-1 < \frac{1}{2}s < 1$,

$$S_2 = 4s^2 \left(1 + \tfrac{1}{2}s + \tfrac{1}{4}s^2 + \tfrac{1}{8}s^3 + \cdots\right)$$
$$= 4s^2 \left(1 + \left(\tfrac{1}{2}s\right) + \left(\tfrac{1}{2}s\right)^2 + \left(\tfrac{1}{2}s\right)^3 + \cdots\right)$$
$$= 4s^2 \times \frac{1}{1 - \frac{1}{2}s}$$
$$= \frac{8s^2}{2-s}. \quad \blacklozenge$$

Activity 8.5   Summing geometric series

Find the sum of each of the following geometric series.

(a) $S_1 = 1 + s^2 + s^4 + \cdots$

(b) $S_2 = 9s + 6s^2 + 4s^3 + \frac{8}{3}s^4 + \cdots$

In each case, state the condition that must be satisfied by s.

Example 8.2 *Series expansion*

Consider the function
$$U(s) = \frac{1}{1 - (2s + s^2)}.$$

This is of the form $1/(1 - x)$ with $x = 2s + s^2$ so, provided that $-1 < 2s + s^2 < 1$, it can be expanded as a power series, as follows:

$$\begin{aligned}
U(s) &= 1 + (2s + s^2) + (2s + s^2)^2 + (2s + s^2)^3 + \cdots \\
&= 1 + 2s + s^2 + (4s^2 + 4s^3 + s^4) + (8s^3 + 12s^4 + 6s^5 + s^6) + \cdots \\
&= 1 + 2s + 5s^2 + 12s^3 + \cdots. \quad \blacklozenge
\end{aligned}$$

Activity 8.6 *Series expansion*

Find the first six non-zero terms in the expansion of the following function as a power series in s:

$$U(s) = \frac{1}{1 - (s^2 + 3s^3)}, \quad \text{for } |s^2 + 3s^3| < 1.$$

The binomial theorem, which is stated in the *Handbook*, provides a formula for expanding a function of the form $(1 + x)^n$ as a power series in x. Note that replacing x with $-x$ and setting $n = -1$ in this formula gives the expansion of $1/(1 - x)$ as a power series in x. The result is $1 + x + x^2 + \cdots$, of course. The binomial theorem is used in M343 to derive a few results, but you will not be expected to use it in assignments or in the examination.

8.3 *Differentiation and integration*

Differentiation

The derivative $f'(x)$ of a function $f(x)$, when it exists, is defined by
$$f'(x) = \lim_{h \to 0} \frac{f(x + h) - f(x)}{h}.$$

This definition is used in the derivation of several results in *Books 2* and *4*.

In M343, you will be required to differentiate functions that involve powers, logarithms and exponentials, using the following rules.

◇   Sum rule: $(f + g)' = f' + g'$.

◇   Constant multiple rule: $(Cf)' = Cf'$, where C is a constant.

◇   Product rule: $(fg)' = f'g + fg'$.

◇   Quotient rule: $\left(\dfrac{f}{g}\right)' = \dfrac{f'g - fg'}{g^2}$.

◇   Composite rule: $(f \circ g)' = (f' \circ g)g'$.

The composite rule is also known as the chain rule.

That is, if $k(x) = f(g(x))$, then $k'(x) = f'(g(x))\,g'(x)$.

A list of standard derivatives is given in Table 8.1.

Table 8.1   Derivatives

Function $f(x)$	Derivative $f'(x)$
1	0
x^n	nx^{n-1}
$\log x \quad (x > 0)$	$\dfrac{1}{x}$
e^{kx}	ke^{kx}

The use of several of the rules is illustrated in Example 8.3.

Example 8.3   Using the rules

(a) If $h(x) = 3x^2 - 5x + 2$, then using the sum rule and the constant multiple rule,

$$h'(x) = 3 \times 2x - 5 = 6x - 5.$$

(b) If $h(x) = \dfrac{1}{5x^2}$, then this can be written as

$$h(x) = \frac{1}{5} \times x^{-2},$$

and hence

$$h'(x) = \frac{1}{5} \times (-2)x^{-3} = -\frac{2}{5} \times \frac{1}{x^3} = -\frac{2}{5x^3}.$$

(c) If $h(x) = 2x\, e^{3x}$, then, using the product rule with $f(x) = 2x$ and $g(x) = e^{3x}$,

$$h'(x) = 2e^{3x} + 2x \times 3e^{3x}$$
$$= (2 + 6x)e^{3x}.$$

$f'(x) = 2, g'(x) = 3e^{3x}.$

(d) Suppose that

$$h(x) = \frac{7 - 2x}{9 - 4x}.$$

Using the quotient rule with $f(x) = 7 - 2x$ and $g(x) = 9 - 4x$,

$$h'(x) = \frac{(-2)(9 - 4x) - (7 - 2x)(-4)}{(9 - 4x)^2}$$
$$= \frac{-18 + 8x + 28 - 8x}{(9 - 4x)^2}$$
$$= \frac{10}{(9 - 4x)^2}.$$

$f'(x) = -2, g'(x) = -4.$

(e) If $h(x) = \log(x^2 + 1)$, then using the composite rule with the outer function being the logarithm and the inner function $g(x) = x^2 + 1$,

$$h'(x) = \frac{1}{x^2 + 1} \times 2x = \frac{2x}{x^2 + 1}. \quad \blacklozenge$$

Differentiate the outer function and multiply by the derivative of the inner function.

Note that part (e) of Example 8.3 is a special case of a useful general result that is given in the table of derivatives in the *Handbook*: if $f(x) = \log g(x)$, then, using the composite rule,

$$f'(x) = \frac{1}{g(x)} \times g'(x) = \frac{g'(x)}{g(x)}.$$

Activity 8.7   Differentiation practice

Differentiate each of the following functions.

(a) $h(x) = \dfrac{7}{x^3}$ (b) $h(x) = \dfrac{3x}{4-x}$

(c) $h(x) = \dfrac{1}{(5-2x)^3}$ (d) $h(x) = \log(1-x)$

Integration

Integration features in M343 more often than differentiation. Finding the mean or variance of a continuous random variable, for instance, requires integration.

See Sections 4 and 5.

Integration is essentially the inverse of differentiation: if $F'(x) = f(x)$, then $F(x)$ is an integral of $f(x)$. Table 8.2 contains a list of standard integrals that are used in M343. The indefinite integral of the function $f(x)$ is

$$\int f(x)\,dx = F(x) + c,$$

where $F(x)$ is any integral of $f(x)$, and c is an arbitrary constant.

Note that since the derivative of a constant is 0, it is important to include an arbitrary constant when finding an indefinite integral.

The constant multiple rule and the sum rule apply to integration:

$$\int k\,f(x)\,dx = k\int f(x)\,dx, \quad k \text{ constant},$$

$$\int (f(x) + g(x))\,dx = \int f(x)\,dx + \int g(x)\,dx.$$

Table 8.2   Standard integrals

Function $f(x)$	Integral $F(x)$
k	kx
x^n $(n \neq -1)$	$\dfrac{x^{n+1}}{n+1}$
$\dfrac{1}{x}$ $(x > 0)$	$\log x$
$\dfrac{g'(x)}{g(x)}$	$\log g(x)$
e^{kx}	$\dfrac{1}{k}e^{kx}$

Example 8.4   Indefinite integrals

(a) Using the constant multiple rule,

$$\int 5x^3\,dx = 5\int x^3\,dx = 5 \times \frac{x^4}{4} + c = \tfrac{5}{4}x^4 + c.$$

(b) Writing $\dfrac{1}{x^3}$ in the form x^n and integrating gives

$$\int \frac{1}{x^3}\,dx = \int x^{-3}\,dx = \frac{x^{-2}}{-2} + c = -\frac{1}{2x^2} + c.$$

When $n = -3$,
$$\frac{x^{n+1}}{n+1} = \frac{x^{-3+1}}{-3+1} = \frac{x^{-2}}{-2}.$$

(c) Using the constant multiple rule,

$$\int \frac{7}{x}\,dx = 7\log x + c. \quad \blacklozenge$$

Example 8.5   Logarithms

Since the derivative of $\log g(x)$ is $g'(x)/g(x)$, it follows that

$$\int \frac{g'(x)}{g(x)}\,dx = \log g(x) + c.$$

Hence, for example,

$$\int \frac{4x}{1+x^2}\,dx = 2\int \frac{2x}{1+x^2}\,dx = 2\log(1+x^2) + c. \quad \blacklozenge$$

Activity 8.8   Indefinite integrals

Find the indefinite integral of each of the following functions.

(a) $6x^2$ (b) $\dfrac{1}{3x^2}$ (c) $\dfrac{1}{1+x}$ (d) $\dfrac{1}{1-x}$ (e) $\dfrac{6}{2x+3}$

The definite integral of the function $f(x)$ from a to b is

$$\int_a^b f(x)\,dx = \big[F(x)\big]_a^b = F(b) - F(a), \tag{8.1}$$

where $F(x)$ is any integral of $f(x)$.

Note that it is not necessary to include an arbitrary constant when finding a definite integral. If you do, it will disappear when you subtract $F(a)$ from $F(b)$.

Example 8.6   Definite integrals

Definite integrals are evaluated using (8.1): an integral $F(x)$ of the function $f(x)$ is found, its value is calculated at the upper limit and at the lower limit, and the difference between these two values is found. For example,

$$\int_1^3 6x\,dx = \big[3x^2\big]_1^3$$
$$= 3 \times 3^2 - 3 \times 1^2$$
$$= 27 - 3$$
$$= 24. \quad \blacklozenge$$

Activity 8.9   Definite integrals

Evaluate the following definite integrals.

(a) $\displaystyle\int_1^2 \dfrac{16}{x^3}\,dx$ (b) $\displaystyle\int_2^4 \dfrac{1}{1+x}\,dx$ (c) $\displaystyle\int_0^2 \dfrac{6}{2x+3}\,dx$

Two other methods for integration are used in M343 (though they are not used very often). These are integration by parts and integration by substitution.

The formula for integration by parts is

$$\int f(x)\,g'(x)\,dx = f(x)\,g(x) - \int f'(x)\,g(x)\,dx. \tag{8.2}$$

If this method is used to find a definite integral, then limits must be included in all the terms:

$$\int_a^b f(x)\,g'(x)\,dx = \big[f(x)\,g(x)\big]_a^b - \int_a^b f'(x)\,g(x)\,dx.$$

Example 8.7   Integration by parts

Integration by parts is required to find the integral of products such as xe^{-3x} and $x^2 e^{-3x}$. When using the method to integrate a product of this type, $f(x)$ is chosen to be the function in the product that becomes simpler when differentiated (provided that the integral of the other function can be found). For example, to integrate xe^{-3x}, let

$$f(x) = x, \quad g'(x) = e^{-3x},$$

so

$$f'(x) = 1, \quad g(x) = -\tfrac{1}{3}e^{-3x}.$$

Then, using (8.2),

$$\int xe^{-3x}\,dx = x \times -\tfrac{1}{3}e^{-3x} - \int 1 \times \left(-\tfrac{1}{3}e^{-3x}\right)dx$$

$$= -\tfrac{1}{3}xe^{-3x} + \tfrac{1}{3}\int e^{-3x}\,dx$$

$$= -\tfrac{1}{3}xe^{-3x} - \tfrac{1}{9}e^{-3x} + c.$$

To integrate $x^2 e^{-3x}$, (8.2) must be used twice. ◆

The integrals of xe^{-3x} and $x^2 e^{-3x}$ are required when finding the mean and variance of an exponential distribution with parameter 3 (see Subsection 5.2).

An arbitrary constant is not needed in $g(x)$.

An arbitrary constant is included only when the last integral is found.

Activity 8.10   Using parts twice

Use integration by parts to find

$$\int_0^\infty x^2 e^{-3x}\,dx.$$

Integration by substitution is used on a very few occasions in M343. The procedure is summarised in the *Handbook*, and is illustrated in Example 8.8.

Example 8.8   Substitution

Integration by substitution is particularly useful when the integrand consists of a product in which one term is a composite function and the other includes the derivative of the inner function of the composite function. For example, it can be used to find the integral

$$I = \int \frac{6x}{(1+x^2)^3}\,dx.$$

The integrand is the product of $\dfrac{1}{(1+x^2)^3}$, which is of the form $f(g(x))$ where $g(x) = 1 + x^2$, and $6x$, which is $3g'(x)$.

To find I, the substitution $u = g(x) = 1 + x^2$ is used. Then

$$\frac{du}{dx} = 2x.$$

Substituting u for $1 + x^2$ in the integrand and $\dfrac{du}{dx}$ for $2x$ gives

$$
\begin{aligned}
I &= \int \frac{3}{u^3}\frac{du}{dx}\,dx \\[2mm]
&= \int \frac{3}{u^3}\,du, \quad \text{replacing } \frac{du}{dx}\,dx \text{ by } du, \\[2mm]
&= \int 3u^{-3}\,du \\[2mm]
&= 3\frac{u^{-2}}{-2} + c \\[2mm]
&= -\frac{3}{2u^2} + c \\[2mm]
&= -\frac{3}{2(1+x^2)^2} + c, \quad \text{substituting for } u \text{ in terms of } x. \quad \blacklozenge
\end{aligned}
$$

Activity 8.11   Substitution

Use the substitution $u = 1 - x$ to find

$$
\int \frac{2x}{(1-x)^2}\,dx.
$$

When integration by substitution is used to find a definite integral from $x = a$ to $x = b$, corresponding limits for u must be found. For the substitution $u = g(x)$, the limits for u corresponding to $x = a$ and $x = b$ are $u = g(a)$ and $u = g(b)$, respectively.

8.4   Ordinary differential equations

Two methods for solving certain types of ordinary differential equations are used in M343: separation of variables and the integrating factor method. These are described briefly in this subsection.

Separation of variables

The method of separation of variables applies to differential equations that can be expressed in the form

$$
\frac{dy}{dx} = f(x)\,g(y),
$$

where $f(x)$ and $g(y)$ are given functions of x and y, respectively. The general solution is obtained by carrying out the two integrations in the equation

$$
\int \frac{1}{g(y)}\,dy = \int f(x)\,dx + c.
$$

The value of the arbitrary constant c can be obtained by using any given initial condition (on y).

Example 8.9   *Separation of variables*

Since $4xy$ is of the form $f(x)\,g(y)$, separation of variables can be used to solve the differential equation

$$\frac{dy}{dx} = 4xy.$$

Separating the variables gives

$$\frac{1}{y}\frac{dy}{dx} = 4x,$$

so

$$\int \frac{1}{y}\frac{dy}{dx}\,dx = \int 4x\,dx,$$

or equivalently,

$$\int \frac{1}{y}\,dy = \int 4x\,dx.$$

Integrating both sides gives

$$\log y = 2x^2 + c,$$

Note that only one arbitrary constant is required.

or

$$y = e^{2x^2+c} = e^{2x^2} \times e^c = Ae^{2x^2},$$

where A is an arbitrary constant.

Given an initial condition, the value of the arbitrary constant can be found. For example, if $y = 3$ when $x = 0$, then

$$3 = Ae^0 = A,$$

and hence, in this case,

$$y = 3e^{2x^2}. \quad \blacklozenge$$

Activity 8.12   *Separation of variables*

Given that $y = 1$ when $x = 1$, solve the differential equation

$$\frac{dy}{dx} = 3x^2y^2.$$

The integrating factor method

The integrating factor method applies to differential equations of the form

$$\frac{dy}{dx} + h(x)\,y = k(x), \tag{8.3}$$

The integrating factor method is used in *Books 2* and *4*.

where $h(x)$ and $k(x)$ are given functions of x. To find the general solution, both sides of the differential equation are first multiplied by the integrating factor $e^{H(x)}$, where $H(x) = \int h(x)\,dx$, to give

$$\frac{d}{dx}(y\,e^{H(x)}) = k(x)\,e^{H(x)}.$$

The general solution is given by

$$y\,e^{H(x)} = \int k(x)\,e^{H(x)}\,dx + c.$$

The value of the arbitrary constant c can be found using any given initial condition.

Example 8.10   Using the integrating factor method

Suppose that

$$\frac{dy}{dx} + 3y = 6,$$

and that $y = 0$ when $x = 0$.

This differential equation is of the form in (8.3). In this case, $h(x) = 3$ and $k(x) = 6$. Therefore

$$H(x) = \int 3\,dx = 3x,$$

You do not need to include an arbitrary constant in $H(x)$.

and hence the integrating factor $e^{H(x)}$ is e^{3x}.

Multiplying both sides of the differential equation by the integrating factor e^{3x} gives

$$e^{3x}\frac{dy}{dx} + 3e^{3x}y = 6e^{3x}.$$

The left-hand side is the derivative of the product $e^{3x}y$, so the equation can be written as

$$\frac{d}{dx}\left(e^{3x}y\right) = 6e^{3x}.$$

Integrating both sides gives

$$e^{3x}y = \int 6e^{3x}\,dx = 2e^{3x} + c,$$

where c is an arbitrary constant. Dividing throughout by e^{3x} gives

$$y = 2 + ce^{-3x}.$$

Since $y = 0$ when $x = 0$,

$$0 = 2 + ce^0 = 2 + c.$$

Therefore $c = -2$, and hence

$$y = 2 - 2e^{-3x}. \quad \blacklozenge$$

Activity 8.13   The integrating factor method

Find the solution of the differential equation

$$\frac{dy}{dx} + 2y = 4xe^{-2x}$$

that satisfies the initial condition $y = 0$ when $x = 0$.

Summary of Section 8

In this section, the following have been reviewed briefly: rules for manipulating powers, logarithms and exponential functions; geometric series; basic differentiation and integration; and two methods for solving ordinary differential equations – separation of variables and the integrating factor method.

Exercises on Section 8

Exercise 8.1   *Evaluating powers*

Calculate the value of each of the following.

(a) 3^3 (b) 3^{-2} (c) $27^{2/3}$ (d) $64^{-1/3}$

Exercise 8.2   *Simplifying expressions*

Simplify each of the following expressions.

(a) $x^3 \times x$ (b) $(x^4)^3$ (c) x^{12}/x^4

Exercise 8.3   *Logarithms and exponentials*

(a) If $y = 2\log 10 - \log 20 + \log 2$, write y as the logarithm of a single number.

(b) Use the rules for manipulating logarithms to find the value of $\log 27/\log 9$.

(c) Simplify the expression

$$\frac{e^{4t} \times \left(e^{-3t}\right)^2}{e^{-5t}}.$$

(d) Write each of the following as expressions that do not involve logarithms or exponential functions.

(i) $y = 3\log(e^{x-2})$ (ii) $y = e^{-4\log(x+2)}$

Exercise 8.4   *Differentiation*

Differentiate each of the following functions.

(a) $h(x) = \dfrac{8}{x^2}$ (b) $h(x) = \dfrac{2+x}{5-2x}$ (c) $h(x) = \log(2x+3)$

Exercise 8.5   *Integration*

Find the following integrals.

(a) $\displaystyle\int \frac{18}{x^4}\, dx$ (b) $\displaystyle\int_1^2 \frac{18}{x^4}\, dx$ (c) $\displaystyle\int \left(\frac{1}{x} - \frac{1}{1-x}\right) dx$

(d) $\displaystyle\int_0^\infty xe^{-2x}\, dx$

Exercise 8.6   *Differential equations*

(a) Given the initial condition $y = 1$ when $x = 0$, solve the differential equation

$$\frac{dy}{dx} = 5y.$$

(b) Given the initial condition $y = 0$ when $x = 0$, solve the differential equation

$$\frac{dy}{dx} + 4y = 2e^{-x}.$$

9   Further exercises on Book 1

Exercise 9.1   Travelling to work

Monica travels to work on foot, by bicycle, by bus or by car, and she uses these methods with probabilities 0.1, 0.3, 0.2 and 0.4, respectively. If she walks, then the probability that she is late for work is 0.35, and the corresponding conditional probabilities of being late if she travels by bicycle, bus or car are 0.1, 0.4 and 0.15, respectively.

(a) Identify the events involved by giving them names, and write down the given probabilities in terms of these names.

(b) Calculate the probability that on any particular day Monica is late for work.

(c) Given that she is late for work one day, calculate the probability that she walked.

(d) Given that she is not late for work, calculate the probability that she walked.

(e) Given that she did not travel to work by car on a particular day, calculate the probability that she was late that day.

Exercise 9.2   Positive reactions to a test

Patients referred to a hospital with a certain symptom are assumed to be suffering from one of three diseases. Let D_1, D_2 and D_3 be the events that a patient is suffering from diseases 1, 2 and 3, respectively. From records, the probabilities that a patient with the symptom is suffering from diseases 1, 2 and 3 have been estimated to be 0.62, 0.27 and 0.11, respectively. Let T be the event that a patient shows a positive reaction when given a particular test. The conditional probabilities of showing a positive reaction to the test, estimated from hospital records, are

$$P(T|D_1) = 0.21, \quad P(T|D_2) = 0.83, \quad P(T|D_3) = 0.68.$$

(a) Find the probability that the next patient referred to the hospital with the symptom will show a positive reaction to the test.

(b) For each of the diseases, calculate the conditional probability that a patient who shows a positive reaction to the test has the disease.

Exercise 9.3   Treatment for a disease

The probability that a patient suffering from a certain disease will react unfavourably to a particular treatment is 0.03. Whether or not a patient reacts unfavourably is independent of whether any other patient reacts unfavourably.

(a) The treatment is given to twelve patients. Calculate the probability that fewer than two patients will react unfavourably.

(b) Calculate the probability that none of the patients in a group of twenty patients will react unfavourably.

(c) Using an appropriate approximate distribution, find the probability that exactly four patients in a group of one hundred patients will react unfavourably to the treatment.

The probability that a patient suffering from the disease will recover completely after receiving treatment is p $(0 < p < 1)$. The treatment is given to n patients in hospital A and m patients in hospital B.

(d) Find the probability that r patients at hospital A will recover.

(e) Find the probability that the total number of patients at the two hospitals who recover will be k.

(f) If it is known that the total number of patients who recovered is k, show that the probability that exactly r of the patients at hospital A recovered is given by

$$\frac{\dbinom{m}{k-r}\dbinom{n}{r}}{\dbinom{m+n}{k}}.$$

Exercise 9.4   *Kicks at goal*

During a practice session, a rugby player takes kicks at goal at distances ranging from 20 metres to 60 metres from the goalposts. Independently for each kick from a distance of y metres, his probability of succeeding is $0.024(60 - y)$.

(a) If the player takes 10 kicks at goal from a distance of 20 metres, calculate the probability that he will have:

  (i) exactly 8 successes;   (ii) at least 8 successes.

(b) Find the value of y to the nearest metre if the kicker has a 99% probability of at least one success in 10 kicks.

(c) The player takes kicks at goal from a distance of 40 metres until he has a success. Calculate the probability that he takes at least three kicks.

(d) Suppose instead that the player takes kicks at goal from a distance of 40 metres until he has two successes. What is the expected number of kicks that he takes?

Exercise 9.5   *Operating costs*

The number of times per day that a loom needs retuning is a random variable R that has a Poisson distribution with parameter $0.1t$, where t is the number of hours of daily operation. The daily cost of operating the loom is $10t + 30R^2$.

(a) Write down $E(R)$ and $E(R^2)$ in terms of t.

(b) Find the expected daily cost of operating the loom.

Exercise 9.6   *The mean of a geometric distribution*

Use the alternative formula (2.4) for the mean of a discrete random variable to find the mean of each of the following variates.

(a) $X \sim G_1(p)$ (b) $X \sim G_0(p)$

Exercise 9.7   *Standard distributions*

For each of the following p.g.f.s, identify the distribution (including the values of any parameters) and use the formulas in Table 8 in the *Handbook* to find the mean and variance.

(a) $\frac{1}{64}(3+s)^3$ (b) $e^{-4t(1-s)}$ (c) $\dfrac{9}{11-2s}$ (d) $\left(\dfrac{5s}{8-3s}\right)^4$

Exercise 9.8   *Using the p.g.f. to find the mean*

Use the p.g.f. to find the mean and variance of a $G_0(p)$ distribution.

Exercise 9.9   Using the p.g.f.

The p.g.f. of the random variable X is

$$\Pi(s) = \frac{5 - 2s}{7 - 4s}.$$

(a) Use the p.g.f. to find the mean and variance of X.

(b) Find $P(X = 0)$.

Exercise 9.10   Sums of independent random variables

The random variable Z is the sum of two independent random variables X and Y. The p.g.f. of Z is

$$\Pi(s) = \frac{2s^4}{3 - s}.$$

Write this p.g.f. as a product of two p.g.f.s, and hence identify the distributions of X and Y.

Exercise 9.11   A continuous random variable

The continuous random variable X has p.d.f.

$$f(x) = k(2 - x), \quad 1 \le x \le 2.$$

(a) Find the value of k.

(b) Calculate the mean and variance of X.

(c) Find the c.d.f. of X.

(d) Use the c.d.f. to calculate $P(X \ge 1.5)$ and $P(1.2 < X < 1.6)$.

Exercise 9.12   Service times

A shop assistant always takes at least two minutes to serve a customer and sometimes takes much longer. The time taken to serve a customer may be modelled by a continuous random variable T with c.d.f.

$$F(t) = 1 - \frac{4}{t^2}, \quad t \ge 2,$$

where t is measured in minutes.

(a) What proportion of customers does the shop assistant take more than five minutes to serve?

(b) Use the alternative formula for the mean (4.4) to calculate the mean of T.

(c) Simulate the time taken to serve a customer, using the number $u = 0.653\,25$, which is a random observation from the uniform distribution $U(0, 1)$. Give your answer in minutes and seconds to the nearest second.

Exercise 9.13   Posting a parcel

It always takes at least two minutes to post a parcel at the local post office, and sometimes it takes longer. In fact, the probability distribution of T, the time taken in minutes, may be written as

$$P(T > t) = \frac{8}{t^3}, \quad t \ge 2.$$

(a) Calculate the probability that it takes more than five minutes to post a parcel.

(b) Calculate the median time that it takes to post a parcel.

(c) Calculate the mean time that it takes to post a parcel.

(d) Calculate the variance of the time that it takes to post a parcel.

(e) Simulate the time that it takes to post a parcel on four successive visits to the post office, using the numbers 0.264, 0.108, 0.560, 0.821, which are random observations from the uniform distribution $U(0, 1)$.

Exercise 9.14   Waiting for a bus

According to the timetable, buses on routes 1, 2 and 3 are scheduled to arrive outside the office where I work every 5, 5 and 10 minutes, respectively. However, when I leave work, they do not arrive regularly due to various factors, including traffic congestion and the large number of passengers at this time of day. I believe that a good model for the intervals between buses on each route is an exponential distribution, and that the mean times between arrivals on the three routes are 5, 5 and 10 minutes. Buses on the three routes operate independently of each other.

(a) According to the proposed model, what is the distribution of the time that I have to wait for a bus to arrive when I leave work?

(b) Assuming that the proposed model is correct, calculate the probability that I will have to wait more than 10 minutes for a bus.

(c) Calculate the probability that I will have to wait less than 20 seconds for a bus.

Exercise 9.15   Simulation schemes

The proportion of tomato plants sold on a market stall that die before producing fruits is $\frac{1}{4}$. The deaths of plants are to be simulated.

(a) Devise a scheme that uses single random digits for simulating the deaths of plants.

(b) Devise a scheme that uses pairs of random digits for simulating the deaths of plants.

Exercise 9.16   Simulation for standard distributions

(a) Use the numbers $u_1 = 0.2690$, $u_2 = 0.0191$ and $u_3 = 0.7943$, which are random observations from $U(0, 1)$, to simulate three observations from the Poisson distribution with mean 1.6.

(b) Use the numbers 0.556 and 3.136, which are random observations from the exponential distribution with mean 1, to simulate two observations from the exponential distribution $M(1.6)$.

(c) Use the numbers 0.9982 and -1.6920, which are random observations from $N(0, 1)$, to simulate two observations from the normal distribution $N(7, 100)$.

Summary of Book 1

Probability underpins all the models for random phenomena discussed in M343. The probability of an event is a number that measures how likely the event is to occur. Rules of probability, including Bayes' formula and the Theorem of Total Probability, are used to calculate probabilities.

A random variable is essentially a quantity that can take any value in a set of values; this set of values is called the range of the random variable. A discrete random variable can take any value in a discrete set of values; its distribution is described using a probability mass function (p.m.f.). A continuous random variable can take any value in an interval of values; its distribution is described using a probability density function (p.d.f.). The cumulative distribution function (c.d.f.) of a random variable X gives the probability that X takes a value less than or equal to x; it is defined for all $x \in \mathbb{R}$, not just for values x in the range of X.

The mean and variance of a discrete random variable can be found using the p.m.f., and the mean and variance of a continuous random variable using the p.d.f. The mean of a non-negative random variable can also be found using the c.d.f.

The probability generating function (p.g.f.) is a useful tool when working with discrete random variables. It encapsulates the distribution of a random variable whose range is a subset of $\{0, 1, 2, \ldots\}$ in a concise mathematical form. No information is lost when a p.g.f. is found: the distribution can be reconstructed from the p.g.f. Much use will be made of p.g.f.s in M343.

Simulation is useful for investigating the behaviour of models for random phenomena. Observations from discrete and continuous distributions can be simulated using tables of random numbers.

Learning outcomes

You have been working to develop the following skills.

◇ Apply rules of probability, including Bayes' formula and the Theorem of Total Probability, to solve problems.

◇ Apply properties of p.m.f.s and c.d.f.s for discrete random variables, and p.d.f.s and c.d.f.s for continuous random variables, to calculate probabilities.

◇ Find the mean and variance of a discrete random variable using its p.m.f., and of a continuous random variable using its p.d.f.

◇ Use the alternative formula for the mean of a non-negative random variable, which involves the c.d.f., to find the mean.

◇ Solve problems involving the following standard distributions: binomial, Poisson, geometric (two versions), negative binomial (two versions), discrete uniform, continuous uniform, exponential, gamma and normal.

◇ Use the tables of discrete and continuous probability distributions given in the *Handbook*.   Tables 8 and 9.

◇ Write down the probability generating function (p.g.f.) for a discrete random variable, and identify a distribution from its p.g.f.

◇ Find the mean and variance of a discrete random variable using the p.g.f.

◇ Obtain the p.g.f. of a sum of independent random variables from the p.g.f.s of the random variables in the sum, and identify the individual random variables in a sum from the p.g.f. of the sum.

◇   Use the table of probabilities and the table of quantiles for the standard
    normal distribution given in the *Handbook*.   Tables 1 and 2.

◇   Use random digits to simulate observations from discrete and continuous
    distributions.   Table 5.

◇   Use relevant tables in the *Handbook* to simulate observations from
    exponential distributions and normal distributions.   Tables 6 and 7.

Solutions to Activities

Solution 1.1

(a) Of the six possible outcomes, three are even numbers – 2, 4 and 6 – so the probability that the score on the die is an even number is

$$P(2 \cup 4 \cup 6) = P(2) + P(4) + P(6) = \tfrac{1}{6} + \tfrac{1}{6} + \tfrac{1}{6} = \tfrac{1}{2}.$$

(b) The score is greater than 4 if it is either 5 or 6, and

$$P(5 \cup 6) = P(5) + P(6) = \tfrac{1}{6} + \tfrac{1}{6} = \tfrac{1}{3}.$$

(c) The score is even and greater than 4 only if it is 6, so the probability required is

$$P(6) = \tfrac{1}{6}.$$

(d) Four of the six possible outcomes give a score that is either even or greater than 4 (or both) – 2, 4, 5 and 6 – so the required probability is

$$\tfrac{1}{6} + \tfrac{1}{6} + \tfrac{1}{6} + \tfrac{1}{6} = \tfrac{2}{3}.$$

Solution 1.2

(a) Using (1.1) gives

$$P(\overline{A}) = 1 - P(A) = 0.5.$$

(b) $P(\overline{B}) = 1 - P(B) = 0.6.$

(c) Using (1.3) gives

$$P(A \cup B) = P(A) + P(B) - P(A \cap B)$$
$$= 0.5 + 0.4 - 0.1 = 0.8.$$

(d) The shaded area in Figure S.1 represents the event $\overline{A} \cap \overline{B}$.

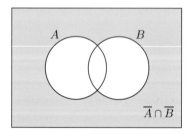

Figure S.1 The event $\overline{A} \cap \overline{B}$

The diagram shows that $\overline{A} \cap \overline{B}$ is the complement of $A \cup B$. Therefore

$$P(\overline{A} \cap \overline{B}) = P(\overline{A \cup B}) = 1 - P(A \cup B) = 0.2.$$

(e) The shaded area in Figure S.2 represents the event $A \cap \overline{B}$.

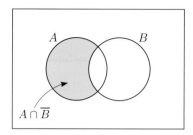

Figure S.2 The event $A \cap \overline{B}$

Hence

$$P(A \cap \overline{B}) = P(A) - P(A \cap B) = 0.5 - 0.1 = 0.4.$$

Alternatively, since A must occur either with B or with $\overline{B}$,

$$P(A) = P(A \cap B) + P(A \cap \overline{B}),$$

and rearranging this leads to the above result.

Solution 1.3

(a) Let A be the event that Swarup listens to the news at five o'clock, and let B be the event that he listens to the news at six o'clock. Then the probabilities can be written as

$$P(A) = 0.45, \quad P(B) = 0.35, \quad P(\overline{A} \cap \overline{B}) = 0.25.$$

(b) The probability that Swarup listens to at least one of the news bulletins is $P(A \cup B)$. Since $A \cup B$ is the complement of $\overline{A} \cap \overline{B}$,

$$P(A \cup B) = 1 - P(\overline{A} \cap \overline{B}) = 1 - 0.25 = 0.75.$$

(c) The probability that Swarup listens to both bulletins is $P(A \cap B)$. Rearranging (1.3) gives

$$P(A \cap B) = P(A) + P(B) - P(A \cup B)$$
$$= 0.45 + 0.35 - 0.75$$
$$= 0.05.$$

Solution 1.4

Each of the probabilities required can be found using the definition of conditional probability (1.4). In Activity 1.2, you found the values of the probabilities $P(\overline{B})$, $P(\overline{A} \cap \overline{B})$ and $P(A \cap \overline{B})$.

(a) $P(A|B) = \dfrac{P(A \cap B)}{P(B)} = \dfrac{0.1}{0.4} = 0.25$

(b) $P(A|\overline{B}) = \dfrac{P(A \cap \overline{B})}{P(\overline{B})} = \dfrac{0.4}{0.6} = \dfrac{2}{3}$

(c) $P(\overline{A}|\overline{B}) = \dfrac{P(\overline{A} \cap \overline{B})}{P(\overline{B})} = \dfrac{0.2}{0.6} = \dfrac{1}{3}$

(d) $P(B|A) = \dfrac{P(B \cap A)}{P(A)} = \dfrac{P(A \cap B)}{P(A)} = \dfrac{0.1}{0.5} = 0.2$

Solution 1.5

From Activity 1.3, $P(A) = 0.45$, $P(B) = 0.35$ and $P(\overline{A} \cap \overline{B}) = 0.25$. The probabilities required can be found using (1.4) and (1.1).

(a) In part (c) of Activity 1.3, you found that $P(A \cap B) = 0.05$, so

$$P(B|A) = \frac{P(B \cap A)}{P(A)} = \frac{P(A \cap B)}{P(A)} = \frac{0.05}{0.45} = \frac{1}{9}.$$

(b) The probability required is

$$P(\overline{B}|\overline{A}) = \frac{P(\overline{B} \cap \overline{A})}{P(\overline{A})}$$
$$= \frac{P(\overline{A} \cap \overline{B})}{1 - P(A)}$$
$$= \frac{0.25}{1 - 0.45} = \frac{0.25}{0.55} = \frac{5}{11}.$$

(c) The probability required is

$$P(A|B) = \frac{P(A \cap B)}{P(B)} = \frac{0.05}{0.35} = \frac{1}{7}.$$

(d) The probability required is $P(\overline{A}|B)$. Given B occurs, either A or $\overline{A}$ must occur, so

$$P(\overline{A}|B) = 1 - P(A|B) = \frac{6}{7}.$$

Solution 1.6

(a) The probabilities may be written as

$$P(S|R) = 0.7, \quad P(S|\overline{R}) = 0.55, \quad P(R) = 0.6.$$

(b) The probability required is $P(R \cap S) = P(S \cap R)$, and using (1.5) gives

$$P(S \cap R) = P(S|R) P(R) = 0.7 \times 0.6 = 0.42.$$

(c) The probability required is $P(\overline{R} \cap \overline{S}) = P(\overline{S} \cap \overline{R})$, and using (1.5) gives

$$P(\overline{S} \cap \overline{R}) = P(\overline{S}|\overline{R}) P(\overline{R}).$$

Given $\overline{R}$ occurs, either S or $\overline{S}$ must occur, so

$$P(\overline{S}|\overline{R}) = 1 - P(S|\overline{R}) = 1 - 0.55 = 0.45.$$

Also,

$$P(\overline{R}) = 1 - P(R) = 1 - 0.6 = 0.4.$$

Therefore

$$P(\overline{R} \cap \overline{S}) = 0.45 \times 0.4 = 0.18.$$

Solution 1.7

(a) The probabilities may be written as

$$P(F) = \tfrac{2}{3}, \quad P(S) = \tfrac{3}{5}, \quad P(S|F) = \tfrac{3}{4}.$$

(b) The probability required is $P(F|S)$. By Bayes' formula,

$$P(F|S) = \frac{P(S|F) P(F)}{P(S)} = \frac{\tfrac{3}{4} \times \tfrac{2}{3}}{\tfrac{3}{5}} = \frac{5}{6}.$$

(c) The first of the two probabilities required is $P(S|\overline{F})$. By Bayes' formula,

$$P(S|\overline{F}) = \frac{P(\overline{F}|S) P(S)}{P(\overline{F})}$$
$$= \frac{(1 - P(F|S)) P(S)}{1 - P(F)},$$
$$= \frac{\left(1 - \tfrac{5}{6}\right) \times \tfrac{3}{5}}{1 - \tfrac{2}{3}}$$
$$= \tfrac{3}{10}.$$

Hence the conditional probability that Anna solved the second problem correctly is $\tfrac{3}{10}$, and the conditional probability that she did not is

$$P(\overline{S}|\overline{F}) = 1 - P(S|\overline{F}) = \tfrac{7}{10}.$$

Solution 1.8

(a) The probabilities are $P(A) = 0.1$ and $P(B) = 0.05$. The events A and B are independent, so

$$P(A \cap B) = P(A) P(B) = 0.1 \times 0.05 = 0.005.$$

(b) The probability that exactly one defect occurs is the probability of 'A but not B' or 'B but not A', that is,

$$P((A \cap \overline{B}) \cup (\overline{A} \cap B)).$$

The two events $A \cap \overline{B}$ and $\overline{A} \cap B$ are mutually exclusive, so this probability is equal to

$$P(A \cap \overline{B}) + P(\overline{A} \cap B).$$

Since the events A and B are independent, so are the events A and $\overline{B}$, and the events $\overline{A}$ and B. Therefore

$$P(A \cap \overline{B}) = P(A) P(\overline{B}) = P(A) (1 - P(B)),$$
$$P(\overline{A} \cap B) = P(\overline{A}) P(B) = (1 - P(A)) P(B).$$

So the required probability is

$$P(A) (1 - P(B)) + (1 - P(A)) P(B)$$
$$= 0.1 \times 0.95 + 0.9 \times 0.05$$
$$= 0.14.$$

There are other ways of calculating this probability. For example, the probability that exactly one defect occurs may be calculated as the probability that at least one defect occurs minus the probability that two defects occur:

$$P(A \cup B) - P(A \cap B).$$

But the probability that at least one defect occurs is equal to 1 minus the probability that no defect occurs, so

$$P(A \cup B) = 1 - P(\overline{A} \cap \overline{B})$$
$$= 1 - P(\overline{A}) P(\overline{B})$$
$$= 1 - 0.9 \times 0.95$$
$$= 0.145.$$

Hence, using the result in part (a), the probability required is given by

$$P(A \cup B) - P(A \cap B) = 0.145 - 0.005 = 0.14.$$

Solution 1.9

(a) The following probabilities can be written down using the information given: $P(R|D) = 0.96$, $P(R|\overline{D}) = 0.03$ and $P(D) = \frac{1}{250} = 0.004$.

(b) The probability required is $P(R)$. By the Theorem of Total Probability,

$$P(R) = P(R|D)\,P(D) + P(R|\overline{D})\,P(\overline{D})$$
$$= 0.96 \times 0.004 + 0.03 \times 0.996$$
$$= 0.033\,72.$$

(c) The probability required is $P(D|R)$. By Bayes' formula,

$$P(D|R) = \frac{P(R|D)\,P(D)}{P(R)}$$
$$= \frac{0.96 \times 0.004}{0.033\,72}$$
$$\simeq 0.1139.$$

Solution 1.10

(a) The following probabilities can be written down using the information given: $P(G) = 0.7$, $P(N) = 0.2$, $P(U) = 0.1$, $P(I|G) = 0.05$, $P(I|N) = 0.95$ and $P(I|U) = 0.25$.

(b) By the Theorem of Total Probability,

$$P(I) = P(I|G)\,P(G) + P(I|N)\,P(N) + P(I|U)\,P(U)$$
$$= 0.05 \times 0.7 + 0.95 \times 0.2 + 0.25 \times 0.1$$
$$= 0.25.$$

(c) By Bayes' formula,

$$P(G|I) = \frac{P(I|G)\,P(G)}{P(I)}$$
$$= \frac{0.05 \times 0.7}{0.25}$$
$$= 0.14.$$

Solution 2.1

(a) The possible values of Y are given in the table below.

Score on die	Value of Y
1, 2 or 3	-1
4 or 5	2
6	3

The range of Y is $\{-1, 2, 3\}$.

(b) The p.m.f. of Y may be written in a table as follows.

y	-1	2	3
$p(y)$	$\frac{1}{2}$	$\frac{1}{3}$	$\frac{1}{6}$

Solution 2.2

(a) $\dbinom{5}{2} = \dfrac{5!}{2!\,3!} = \dfrac{1 \times 2 \times 3 \times 4 \times 5}{(1 \times 2)(1 \times 2 \times 3)} = \dfrac{4 \times 5}{1 \times 2} = 10$

(b) $\dbinom{8}{6} = \dfrac{8!}{6!\,2!} = \dfrac{1 \times 2 \times \cdots \times 6 \times 7 \times 8}{(1 \times 2 \times \cdots \times 6)(1 \times 2)}$
$$= \dfrac{7 \times 8}{1 \times 2} = 28$$

(c) $\dbinom{10}{7} = \dfrac{10!}{7!\,3!} = \dfrac{1 \times 2 \times \cdots \times 7 \times 8 \times 9 \times 10}{(1 \times 2 \times \cdots \times 7)(1 \times 2 \times 3)}$
$$= \dfrac{8 \times 9 \times 10}{1 \times 2 \times 3} = 120$$

(d) $\dbinom{9}{1} = \dfrac{9!}{1!\,8!} = \dfrac{1 \times 2 \times \cdots \times 8 \times 9}{(1)(1 \times 2 \times \cdots \times 8)} = 9$

(e) $\dbinom{6}{3} = \dfrac{6!}{3!\,3!} = \dfrac{1 \times 2 \times 3 \times 4 \times 5 \times 6}{(1 \times 2 \times 3)(1 \times 2 \times 3)}$
$$= \dfrac{4 \times 5 \times 6}{1 \times 2 \times 3} = 20$$

(f) $\dbinom{7}{0} = \dfrac{7!}{0!\,7!} = \dfrac{7!}{1 \times 7!} = 1$

Solution 2.3

(a) $P(Y = 4) = \dbinom{7}{4} 0.3^4\,0.7^3$
$$= 35 \times 0.3^4 \times 0.7^3$$
$$\simeq 0.0972$$

(b) $P(V = 3) = \dbinom{10}{3} 0.6^3\,0.4^7$
$$= 120 \times 0.6^3 \times 0.4^7$$
$$\simeq 0.0425$$

(c) $P(W = 10) = \dbinom{14}{10} 0.42^{10}\,0.58^4$
$$= 1001 \times 0.42^{10} \times 0.58^4$$
$$\simeq 0.0193$$

(d) $P(Z \le 2) = P(Z = 0) + P(Z = 1) + P(Z = 2)$
$$= 0.015\,625 + 0.093\,75 + 0.234\,375$$
$$= 0.343\,75 \simeq 0.3438.$$

Alternatively, working in fractions,

$$P(Z \le 2) = \tfrac{1}{64} + \tfrac{6}{64} + \tfrac{15}{64} = \tfrac{22}{64} = \tfrac{11}{32}.$$

Solution 2.4

(a) The number of shots required to hit the bull's-eye has a geometric distribution, $X \sim G_1(0.3)$, so

$$P(X = 3) = 0.7^2 \times 0.3 = 0.147.$$

(b) The probability required is

$$P(X > 5) = P(X \ge 6)$$
$$= 0.7^5, \quad \text{using (2.2)},$$
$$= 0.168\,07 \simeq 0.1681.$$

Solution 2.5

If N represents the number of withdrawals that Sarah makes before she makes a mistake, then $N \sim G_0(0.8)$. The probability required is $P(N < 5)$. This can be calculated directly as follows:

$$P(N < 5) = \sum_{n=0}^{4} P(N = n)$$
$$= 0.2 + 0.2 \times 0.8 + 0.2 \times 0.8^2$$
$$+ 0.2 \times 0.8^3 + 0.2 \times 0.8^4$$
$$\simeq 0.6723.$$

Alternatively, $P(N < 5) = 1 - P(N \geq 5)$, and $N \geq 5$ implies that all the first five attempts are successful. Hence

$$P(N < 5) = 1 - 0.8^5 \simeq 0.6723.$$

Solution 2.6

If X represents the number of shots required to hit the bull's-eye three times, then X has a negative binomial distribution with parameters 3 and 0.3, with range $\{3, 4, \ldots\}$, so

$$P(X = 7) = \binom{6}{2} 0.3^3 \, 0.7^4 \simeq 0.0972.$$

Solution 2.7

(a) If $X \sim \text{Poisson}(2.5)$, then
$$P(X = 0) = e^{-2.5} \simeq 0.0821.$$

(b) The probability required is
$$P(X > 3) = 1 - (P(X = 0) + P(X = 1)$$
$$+ P(X = 2) + P(X = 3))$$
$$\simeq 1 - (0.0821 + 0.2052 + 0.2565 + 0.2138)$$
$$= 1 - 0.7576$$
$$= 0.2424.$$

Solution 2.8

(a) If X is the number of men with the blood condition in a group of 100 men, then $X \sim B(100, 0.04)$.

(b) Since n is large and p is small, a Poisson approximation may be used:
$$X \approx \text{Poisson}(100 \times 0.04) = \text{Poisson}(4).$$
The probability required is
$$P(X < 3) = P(X = 0) + P(X = 1) + P(X = 2)$$
$$\simeq e^{-4} + 4e^{-4} + 8e^{-4}$$
$$\simeq 0.2381.$$

(Using the binomial distribution, you should obtain 0.2321 for this probability.)

Solution 2.9

(a) $X \sim B(1, 0.2)$

(b) $Y \sim G_1(0.2)$

(c) $W \sim B(50, 0.8)$

(d) V has a negative binomial distribution with parameters 3 and 0.2, and range $\{0, 1, \ldots\}$.

Solution 2.10

Using (2.3), the expected value of X is
$$E(X) = 1 \times 0.4 + 2 \times 0.3 + 3 \times 0.2 + 4 \times 0.1$$
$$= 2.$$

Solution 2.11

(a) The values of the c.d.f. are given in the table below.

x	0	1	2	3	4
$F(x)$	0	0	0.3	0.8	1

(b) Using (2.4), the expected value of X is
$$E(X) = \sum_{x=0}^{\infty}(1 - F(x))$$
$$= (1 - 0) + (1 - 0) + (1 - 0.3) + (1 - 0.8)$$
$$+ 0 + \cdots$$
$$= 1 + 1 + 0.7 + 0.2$$
$$= 2.9.$$

Solution 2.12

In this case, the variance may be found more easily using (2.8) than (2.7). Using (2.5),
$$E(X^2) = 1^2 \times 0.4 + 2^2 \times 0.3 + 3^2 \times 0.2 + 4^2 \times 0.1 = 5.$$
From the solution to Activity 2.10, $\mu = E(X) = 2$, so using (2.8),
$$V(X) = E(X^2) - \mu^2 = 5 - 2^2 = 1.$$

Solution 2.13

(a) For a Poisson variate with parameter μ, the mean and variance are both equal to μ, so
$$E(X) = V(X) = \mu_1, \quad E(Y) = V(Y) = \mu_2.$$
Using (2.9) and (2.10),
$$E(X + Y) = \mu_1 + \mu_2,$$
$$V(X + Y) = \mu_1 + \mu_2.$$

(b) If $X \sim G_1(p)$, then $E(X) = 1/p$ and $V(X) = q/p^2$, so
$$E(X) = E(Y) = 3,$$
$$V(X) = V(Y) = \tfrac{2}{3}/\left(\tfrac{1}{3}\right)^2 = 6.$$
Hence
$$E(X + Y) = 3 + 3 = 6,$$
$$V(X + Y) = 6 + 6 = 12.$$

Solution 3.1

(a) $\Pi(s) = 0.5s + 0.4s^2 + 0.1s^3$.

(b) Since $p(1) = p(2) = \cdots = p(6) = \frac{1}{6}$, the p.g.f. is
$$\Pi(s) = \tfrac{1}{6}s + \tfrac{1}{6}s^2 + \tfrac{1}{6}s^3 + \tfrac{1}{6}s^4 + \tfrac{1}{6}s^5 + \tfrac{1}{6}s^6.$$

(c) Since $p(7) = P(X = 7) = 1$ and $p(x) = P(X = x) = 0$ otherwise, the p.g.f. of X is
$$\Pi(s) = 0s^0 + 0s^1 + \cdots + 1s^7 + 0s^8 + \cdots = s^7.$$

Solution 3.2

(a) The p.g.f. can be rewritten as
$$\Pi(s) = \tfrac{1}{4}s + \tfrac{1}{4}s^2 + \tfrac{1}{2}s^3.$$
So the p.m.f. is given by
$$p(1) = \tfrac{1}{4}, \quad p(2) = \tfrac{1}{4}, \quad p(3) = \tfrac{1}{2}.$$
(The probability $p(x)$ is 0 otherwise.)

(b) The p.g.f. can be rewritten as
$$\Pi(s) = \tfrac{1}{9}(4 + 4s^2 + s^4) = \tfrac{4}{9} + \tfrac{4}{9}s^2 + \tfrac{1}{9}s^4.$$
The probabilities $p(x) = P(X = x)$ can be picked out:
$$p(0) = \tfrac{4}{9}, \quad p(2) = \tfrac{4}{9}, \quad p(4) = \tfrac{1}{9}.$$
(The probability $p(x)$ is 0 otherwise.)

Solution 3.3

The p.m.f. of a $G_0(p)$ variate is
$$p(x) = p^x q, \quad x = 0, 1, \ldots .$$
Therefore the p.g.f. is
$$\Pi(s) = \sum_{x=0}^{\infty} p^x q s^x$$
$$= q(1 + ps + (ps)^2 + \cdots)$$
$$= \frac{q}{1 - ps}.$$

Solution 3.4

The p.m.f. of a Poisson(μ) variate is
$$p(x) = \frac{e^{-\mu}\mu^x}{x!}, \quad x = 0, 1, \ldots .$$
So the p.g.f. is given by
$$\Pi(s) = \sum_{x=0}^{\infty} \frac{e^{-\mu}\mu^x}{x!} s^x$$
$$= e^{-\mu} \sum_{x=0}^{\infty} \frac{(\mu s)^x}{x!}$$
$$= e^{-\mu} e^{\mu s}$$
$$= e^{-\mu(1-s)}.$$

Solution 3.5

(a) The p.g.f. of a Poisson(μ) variate is
$$\Pi(s) = e^{-\mu(1-s)}.$$
So, if $X \sim$ Poisson(4), then
$$\Pi(s) = e^{-4(1-s)}.$$

(b) The p.g.f. of a $G_1(p)$ variate is
$$\Pi(s) = \frac{ps}{1 - qs}.$$
Putting $p = \tfrac{1}{3}$ and $q = \tfrac{2}{3}$ in this formula gives
$$\Pi(s) = \frac{\tfrac{1}{3}s}{1 - \tfrac{2}{3}s} = \frac{s}{3 - 2s}.$$

Solution 3.6

(a) $\Pi(s) = \tfrac{1}{81}(2 + s)^4 = \left(\tfrac{2}{3} + \tfrac{1}{3}s\right)^4$, so $X \sim B\left(4, \tfrac{1}{3}\right)$.

(b) $\Pi(s) = e^{-\frac{1}{3}(1-s)t} = e^{-\frac{1}{3}t(1-s)}$, so
$X \sim$ Poisson$\left(\tfrac{1}{3}t\right)$.

(c) $\Pi(s) = \dfrac{1}{5 - 4s} = \dfrac{\tfrac{1}{5}}{1 - \tfrac{4}{5}s}$, so $X \sim G_0\left(\tfrac{4}{5}\right)$.

(d) $\Pi(s) = \dfrac{4}{(3 - s)^2} = \left(\dfrac{2}{3 - s}\right)^2 = \left(\dfrac{\tfrac{2}{3}}{1 - \tfrac{1}{3}s}\right)^2.$

This is the p.g.f. of a negative binomial distribution with parameters $r = 2$, $p = \tfrac{1}{3}$ and range $\{0, 1, \ldots\}$.

Solution 3.7

(a) The p.g.f. of a Poisson(μ) variate is
$$\Pi(s) = e^{-\mu(1-s)},$$
so
$$\Pi'(s) = \mu e^{-\mu(1-s)},$$
$$\Pi''(s) = \mu^2 e^{-\mu(1-s)}.$$
Putting $s = 1$ and using Formulas (3.4) and (3.5) gives
$$E(X) = \Pi'(1) = \mu,$$
$$V(X) = \Pi''(1) + \mu - \mu^2 = \mu^2 + \mu - \mu^2 = \mu.$$

(b) The p.g.f. of a $G_1(p)$ variate is
$$\Pi(s) = \frac{ps}{1 - qs},$$
so
$$\Pi'(s) = \frac{p}{(1 - qs)^2},$$
$$\Pi''(s) = \frac{2pq}{(1 - qs)^3}.$$
Putting $s = 1$ gives
$$\mu = \Pi'(1) = \frac{p}{(1 - q)^2} = \frac{p}{p^2} = \frac{1}{p},$$
$$\sigma^2 = \Pi''(1) + \mu - \mu^2$$
$$= \frac{2pq}{(1 - q)^3} + \frac{1}{p} - \frac{1}{p^2}$$
$$= \frac{2q}{p^2} + \frac{1}{p} - \frac{1}{p^2}$$
$$= \frac{2q + p - 1}{p^2}$$
$$= \frac{q}{p^2}.$$

Solution 3.8

The p.g.f.s of X and Y are
$$\Pi_X(s) = e^{-\mu_1(1-s)}, \quad \Pi_Y(s) = e^{-\mu_2(1-s)}.$$
Therefore the p.g.f. of $Z = X + Y$ is
$$\Pi_Z(s) = \Pi_X(s)\,\Pi_Y(s)$$
$$= e^{-\mu_1(1-s)} e^{-\mu_2(1-s)}$$
$$= e^{-(\mu_1 + \mu_2)(1-s)}.$$

This is the p.g.f. of a Poisson distribution with parameter $\mu_1 + \mu_2$, so $Z \sim$ Poisson($\mu_1 + \mu_2$).

Solution 3.9

The p.g.f. can be written as

$$\Pi_Z(s) = s^8 \times (0.6 + 0.4s)^4 = \Pi_X(s) \times \Pi_Y(s).$$

Hence $Z = X + Y$, where X is a degenerate random variable that takes the value 8, and Y has the binomial distribution $B(4, 0.4)$.

Therefore $Z = 8 + Y$, where $Y \sim B(4, 0.4)$.

Solution 3.10

The p.g.f. of a $G_0(p)$ variate is

$$\Pi(s) = \frac{q}{1 - ps}.$$

Hence the p.g.f. of $Z = X_1 + X_2 + \cdots + X_n$ is

$$\Pi_Z(s) = \frac{q}{1 - ps} \times \frac{q}{1 - ps} \times \cdots \times \frac{q}{1 - ps}$$

$$= \left(\frac{q}{1 - ps}\right)^n.$$

This is the p.g.f. of a negative binomial distribution with range $\{0, 1, \ldots\}$ and parameters n and p.

Solution 3.11

(a) The p.g.f. of X is

$$\Pi_X(s) = \frac{0.6}{1 - 0.4s},$$

so, using (3.9),

$$\Pi_Y(s) = \frac{0.6}{1 - 0.4s^5}.$$

(b) The p.g.f. of $Y = 2X$ is obtained by replacing s with s^2 in $\Pi_X(s)$, so

$$\Pi_Y(s) = \frac{2 + s^2}{5 - 2s^2}.$$

Solution 4.1

(a) The probability that an oil change takes six minutes or less is given by

$$P(T \le 6) = F(6) = (36 - 4)/96 = \tfrac{1}{3}.$$

(b) If $P(T \le c) = 0.9$, then

$$(c^2 - 4)/96 = 0.9,$$

so

$$c^2 = 90.4,$$

and hence

$$c \simeq 9.508.$$

That is, the probability that the oil change will be completed within about $9\tfrac{1}{2}$ minutes is 0.9.

(c) Note that the values of $F(t)$ lie between 0 and 1, and $F(t)$ is non-decreasing. The c.d.f. is shown in Figure S.3.

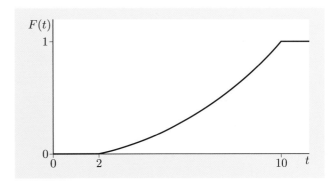

Figure S.3 The c.d.f. of T

Solution 4.2

(a) Differentiating $F(t)$ gives

$$F'(t) = \begin{cases} 0, & t < 2, \ t > 10, \\ \dfrac{t}{48}, & 2 < t < 10. \end{cases}$$

The derivative cannot be calculated at $t = 2$ or $t = 10$. For convenience, f will be specified by $f(t) = t/48$ at $t = 2$ and $t = 10$, so

$$f(t) = \frac{t}{48}, \quad 2 \le t \le 10.$$

(b) The probability required is

$$P(6 < T < 7) = \int_6^7 f(t)\, dt$$

$$= \int_6^7 \frac{t}{48}\, dt$$

$$= \left[\frac{t^2}{96}\right]_6^7$$

$$= \tfrac{13}{96}.$$

(c) A sketch of the p.d.f. is shown in Figure S.4.

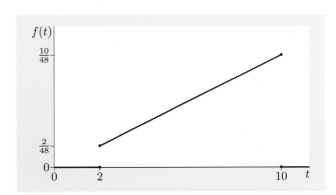

Figure S.4 The p.d.f. of T

Solution 4.3

For $w < 2$, $F(w) = 0$.

For $2 \le w \le 4$,

$$F(w) = \int_{-\infty}^{w} f(u)\,du$$

$$= \int_{2}^{w} \left(2 - \tfrac{1}{2}u\right) du$$

$$= \left[2u - \tfrac{1}{4}u^2\right]_2^w$$

$$= 2w - \tfrac{1}{4}w^2 - (4 - 1)$$

$$= 2w - \tfrac{1}{4}w^2 - 3.$$

For $w > 4$, $F(w) = 1$.

Therefore the c.d.f. of W is

$$F(w) = \begin{cases} 0, & w < 2, \\ 2w - \tfrac{1}{4}w^2 - 3, & 2 \le w \le 4, \\ 1, & w > 4. \end{cases}$$

Solution 4.4

The mean of W is

$$\mu = E(W) = \int_2^4 w\left(2 - \tfrac{1}{2}w\right) dw$$

$$= \int_2^4 \left(2w - \tfrac{1}{2}w^2\right) dw$$

$$= \left[w^2 - \tfrac{1}{6}w^3\right]_2^4$$

$$= \left(16 - \tfrac{32}{3}\right) - \left(4 - \tfrac{4}{3}\right)$$

$$= 2\tfrac{2}{3}.$$

Also,

$$E(W^2) = \int_2^4 w^2\left(2 - \tfrac{1}{2}w\right) dw$$

$$= \int_2^4 \left(2w^2 - \tfrac{1}{2}w^3\right) dw$$

$$= \left[\tfrac{2}{3}w^3 - \tfrac{1}{8}w^4\right]_2^4$$

$$= \left(\tfrac{128}{3} - 32\right) - \left(\tfrac{16}{3} - 2\right)$$

$$= 7\tfrac{1}{3}.$$

Therefore the variance of W is

$$V(W) = E(W^2) - \mu^2 = 7\tfrac{1}{3} - \left(2\tfrac{2}{3}\right)^2 = \tfrac{2}{9}.$$

Solution 4.5

The mean time in minutes is

$$E(T) = \int_{-\infty}^{\infty} t\,f(t)\,dt$$

$$= \int_2^{10} \tfrac{t^2}{48}\,dt$$

$$= \tfrac{1}{144}\left[t^3\right]_2^{10}$$

$$= 6\tfrac{8}{9}.$$

That is, the mean time taken to change the oil in a car is approximately 6 minutes 53 seconds.

The variance is given by

$$V(T) = E(T^2) - \mu^2,$$

where

$$E(T^2) = \int_2^{10} \tfrac{t^3}{48}\,dt = 52.$$

Hence

$$V(T) = 52 - \left(6\tfrac{8}{9}\right)^2 \simeq 4.543 \text{ (minutes)}^2.$$

Solution 4.6

The mean lifetime of the birds (in years) is

$$E(T) = \int_0^{\infty} (1 - F(t))\,dt$$

$$= \int_0^{\infty} \left(1 - \left(1 - \frac{1}{(t+1)^2}\right)\right) dt$$

$$= \int_0^{\infty} \frac{1}{(t+1)^2}\,dt$$

$$= \left[-\frac{1}{t+1}\right]_0^{\infty}$$

$$= 1.$$

Solution 4.7

The mean time for an oil change (in minutes) is

$$E(T) = \int_0^{\infty} (1 - F(t))\,dt$$

$$= \int_0^2 1\,dt + \int_2^{10} \frac{100 - t^2}{96}\,dt + \int_{10}^{\infty} 0\,dt$$

$$= 2 + \left[\frac{100t - t^3/3}{96}\right]_2^{10}$$

$$= 2 + 4\tfrac{8}{9} = 6\tfrac{8}{9},$$

as you found in Activity 4.5 using (4.1).

Solution 4.8

The median m satisfies

$$F(m) = \tfrac{1}{9}m^2 = \tfrac{1}{2},$$

so

$$m^2 = 4.5,$$

and hence

$$m = \sqrt{4.5} \simeq 2.121.$$

The 0.99-quantile $q_{0.99}$ is the solution of

$$F(q_{0.99}) = \tfrac{1}{9}q_{0.99}^2 = 0.99,$$

so

$$q_{0.99}^2 = 9 \times 0.99 = 8.91,$$

and hence

$$q_{0.99} = \sqrt{8.91} \simeq 2.985.$$

Solution 5.1

When $X \sim U(a,b)$, $E(X) = (a+b)/2$ and

$$E(X^2) = \int_a^b \frac{x^2}{b-a}\, dx$$

$$= \frac{1}{b-a} \left[\tfrac{1}{3} x^3 \right]_a^b$$

$$= \frac{b^3 - a^3}{3(b-a)}.$$

Therefore

$$V(X) = E(X^2) - \mu^2$$

$$= \frac{b^3 - a^3}{3(b-a)} - \frac{(a+b)^2}{4}$$

$$= \frac{4(b^3 - a^3) - 3(b-a)(a+b)^2}{12(b-a)}$$

$$= \tfrac{1}{12}(b-a)^2.$$

Solution 5.2

(a) $F(x) = \int_0^x \lambda e^{-\lambda u}\, du$

$$= \left[-e^{-\lambda u} \right]_0^x$$

$$= 1 - e^{-\lambda x}, \quad x \geq 0.$$

(b) $E(X) = \int_0^\infty (1 - F(x))\, dx,$

$$= \int_0^\infty e^{-\lambda x}\, dx$$

$$= \left[-\frac{1}{\lambda} e^{-\lambda x} \right]_0^\infty$$

$$= \frac{1}{\lambda}.$$

The mean of the exponential distribution is $1/\lambda$.

(c) To find $E(X^2)$, integration by parts must be used twice:

$$E(X^2) = \int_0^\infty x^2 \lambda e^{-\lambda x}\, dx$$

$$= \left[-x^2 e^{-\lambda x} \right]_0^\infty + \int_0^\infty 2x e^{-\lambda x}\, dx$$

$$= 0 + 2 \int_0^\infty x e^{-\lambda x}\, dx$$

$$= 2 \left(\left[-\frac{1}{\lambda} x e^{-\lambda x} \right]_0^\infty + \int_0^\infty \frac{1}{\lambda} e^{-\lambda x}\, dx \right)$$

$$= 0 + 2 \left[-\frac{1}{\lambda^2} e^{-\lambda x} \right]_0^\infty$$

$$= \frac{2}{\lambda^2}.$$

So

$$V(X) = E(X^2) - \mu^2 = \frac{2}{\lambda^2} - \frac{1}{\lambda^2} = \frac{1}{\lambda^2}.$$

It follows that the standard deviation is $1/\lambda$, and hence for an exponential distribution the mean is equal to the standard deviation.

Solution 5.3

(a) The memoryless property must be used here: the lengths of time that the assistants have been attending to their current customers are irrelevant. Hence, since the mean of $M(\lambda)$ is $1/\lambda$, the distribution of T_i, the time until assistant i finishes serving their current customer, is $M(\lambda_i)$, where $\lambda_1 = 1$, $\lambda_2 = \frac{2}{3}$, $\lambda_3 = \frac{1}{3}$. The minimum of T_1, T_2 and T_3 has an exponential distribution with parameter

$$\lambda = \lambda_1 + \lambda_2 + \lambda_3 = 1 + \tfrac{2}{3} + \tfrac{1}{3} = 2.$$

That is, $T \sim M(2)$.

(b) The probability required is (working in minutes)

$$P\!\left(T < \tfrac{1}{3}\right) = 1 - e^{-2/3} \simeq 0.4866.$$

Solution 5.4

(a) By the memoryless property, the time T_1 until the service of the current customer is completed is exponentially distributed with mean 1.5 minutes (and hence parameter $\frac{2}{3}$). The total time that you will have to wait is

$$W = T_1 + T_2 + T_3,$$

where $T_i \sim M\!\left(\frac{2}{3}\right)$, $i = 1, 2, 3$, and the T_i are independent. Therefore

$$W \sim \Gamma\!\left(3, \tfrac{2}{3}\right).$$

(b) The mean of $\Gamma(n, \lambda)$ is n/λ, and the variance is n/λ^2. Therefore

$$E(W) = \frac{3}{2/3} = 4.5 \text{ minutes,}$$

$$V(W) = \frac{3}{(2/3)^2} = 6.75 \text{ (minutes)}^2,$$

and hence the standard deviation of W is $\sqrt{6.75} \simeq 2.60$ minutes.

Solution 5.5

(a) The probability required is

$$P(15 < X < 18)$$

$$= P\!\left(\frac{15 - 16}{\sqrt{5}} < \frac{X - 16}{\sqrt{5}} < \frac{18 - 16}{\sqrt{5}} \right)$$

$$\simeq P(-0.45 < Z < 0.89)$$

$$= \Phi(0.89) - \Phi(-0.45)$$

$$= 0.8133 - (1 - 0.6736)$$

$$= 0.8133 - 0.3264$$

$$\simeq 0.487.$$

(b) If $P(X > c) = 0.1$, then $P(X \leq c) = 0.9$, and hence

$$P\left(Z \leq \frac{c - 16}{\sqrt{5}}\right) = 0.9.$$

From Table 2 in the *Handbook*,

$$P(Z \leq 1.282) = 0.9,$$

so

$$\frac{c - 16}{\sqrt{5}} = 1.282.$$

Hence

$$c = 16 + 1.282 \times \sqrt{5} \simeq 18.87.$$

Solution 5.6

(a) By the central limit theorem,

$$\overline{X} \approx N\left(2, \tfrac{3}{90}\right) = N\left(2, \tfrac{1}{30}\right).$$

(b) $T \approx N(90 \times 2, 90 \times 3) = N(180, 270).$

(c) The probability required is

$$P(T > 200) \simeq P\left(Z > \frac{200 - 180}{\sqrt{270}}\right)$$

$$\simeq P(Z > 1.22)$$

$$= 1 - \Phi(1.22)$$

$$= 1 - 0.8888$$

$$= 0.1112 \simeq 0.111.$$

Solution 5.7

(a) For $\chi^2(5)$, $q_{0.01} = 0.554$ and $q_{0.95} = 11.07$.

(b) For $\chi^2(10)$, $q_{0.005} = 2.16$ and $q_{0.975} = 20.48$.

(c) For $\chi^2(23)$, $q_{0.05} = 13.09$ and $q_{0.995} = 44.18$.

Solution 6.1

(a) For the given distribution, for $x \geq 0$,

$$F(x) = \int_0^x 4u e^{-2u^2}\, du = 1 - e^{-2x^2}.$$

(b) Solving $F(x) = 0.4287$ gives

$$e^{-2x^2} = 0.5713,$$

so

$$2x^2 \simeq 0.5598$$

and hence, since $x \geq 0$,

$$x \simeq 0.529.$$

The simulated observation is 0.529.

Solution 6.2

Since the mean length of a call is 5 minutes, the parameter λ of the exponential distribution is $\tfrac{1}{5}$, and hence the c.d.f. of T, the length of a call, is

$$F(t) = 1 - e^{-t/5}, \quad t \geq 0.$$

Solving $F(t) = u$ gives

$$t = -5 \log(1 - u).$$

So the four simulated times are

$$t_1 = -5 \log(1 - 0.406\,38) \text{ minutes}$$
$$\simeq 2 \text{ minutes } 36 \text{ seconds},$$

$$t_2 = -5 \log(1 - 0.794\,67) \text{ minutes}$$
$$\simeq 7 \text{ minutes } 55 \text{ seconds},$$

$$t_3 = -5 \log(1 - 0.534\,23) \text{ minutes}$$
$$\simeq 3 \text{ minutes } 49 \text{ seconds},$$

$$t_4 = -5 \log(1 - 0.834\,90) \text{ minutes}$$
$$\simeq 9 \text{ minutes } 0 \text{ seconds}.$$

In M343 'log' is used to indicate a logarithm to base e. You may be familiar with the alternatives 'ln' or '$\log_e$'.

Take care that you use the correct button on your calculator when doing calculations involving natural logarithms (base e); on many calculators, this is the key labelled 'ln'.

Solution 6.3

Since the mean of the exponential distribution is 5, the numbers from Table 6.2 must be multiplied by 5 to give simulated times in minutes. The four simulated times are

$$t_1 = 5 \times 1.2891 \text{ minutes}$$
$$\simeq 6 \text{ minutes } 27 \text{ seconds},$$

$$t_2 = 5 \times 0.9435 \text{ minutes}$$
$$\simeq 4 \text{ minutes } 43 \text{ seconds},$$

$$t_3 = 5 \times 1.0012 \text{ minutes}$$
$$\simeq 5 \text{ minutes } 0 \text{ seconds},$$

$$t_4 = 5 \times 2.2380 \text{ minutes}$$
$$\simeq 11 \text{ minutes } 11 \text{ seconds}.$$

Solution 6.4

Since $\mu = 4$ and $\sigma = \sqrt{9} = 3$, for each number z from Table 6.3, an observation from $N(4, 9)$ can be simulated by calculating $x = 3z + 4$. The three simulated observations from $N(4, 9)$ are

$$x_1 = 3 \times 0.4776 + 4 = 5.4328 \simeq 5.433,$$

$$x_2 = 3 \times 0.0094 + 4 = 4.0282 \simeq 4.028,$$

$$x_3 = 3 \times -1.4396 + 4 = -0.3188 \simeq -0.319.$$

Solution 6.5

(a) One possible scheme is given in Table S.1. There are many other possibilities.

Table S.1　A simulation scheme

Digit	Outcome
1, 2, 3, 4, 5, 6	Alan wins (W)
7, 8, 9	Alan loses (L)
0	Ignore (select next digit)

(b) Using the scheme in Table S.1 gives the following simulation.

Digit	4	0	6	3	8	7	9	4	6
Outcome	W	–	W	W	L	L	L	W	W

In the simulation, Alan wins five out of the eight games.

Solution 6.6

One possible scheme is given in Table S.2.

Table S.2　A simulation scheme

Digits	Outcome
01, …, 65	Alan wins
66, …, 99, 00	Alan loses

Solution 6.7

Values of the p.m.f. and the c.d.f. of a Poisson distribution with mean 3.8 are given in Table S.3. The values of the c.d.f. were obtained by summing values of the p.m.f.

Table S.3　The p.m.f. and c.d.f. of Poisson(3.8)

x	0	1	2	3	4	5	$\cdots$
$p(x)$	0.0224	0.0850	0.1615	0.2046	0.1944	0.1477	$\cdots$
$F(x)$	0.0224	0.1074	0.2689	0.4735	0.6679	0.8156	$\cdots$

Since

$$F(0) < 0.092\,40 \leq F(1),$$

the first simulated value is $x_1 = 1$. Similarly,

$$x_2 = 3, \quad x_3 = 5, \quad x_4 = 2, \quad x_5 = 2.$$

Solution 7.1

Summing rows and columns gives the following marginal distributions.

x	1	2
$p_X(x)$	0.5	0.5

y	0	1	2
$p_Y(y)$	0.2	0.5	0.3

Solution 7.2

By definition,

$$p(y|0) = \frac{p(0, y)}{p_X(0)},$$

so

$$p(0|0) = \frac{p(0,0)}{p_X(0)} = \frac{0.1}{0.6} = \frac{1}{6},$$

$$p(1|0) = \frac{p(0,1)}{p_X(0)} = \frac{0.4}{0.6} = \frac{2}{3},$$

$$p(2|0) = \frac{p(0,2)}{p_X(0)} = \frac{0.1}{0.6} = \frac{1}{6}.$$

So the conditional p.m.f. is as follows.

y	0	1	2
$p(y|0)$	$\frac{1}{6}$	$\frac{2}{3}$	$\frac{1}{6}$

Solution 7.3

By definition,

$$p(x|1) = \frac{p(x, 1)}{p_Y(1)},$$

so

$$p(0|1) = \frac{p(0,1)}{p_Y(1)} = \frac{0.4}{0.6} = \frac{2}{3},$$

$$p(3|1) = \frac{p(3,1)}{p_Y(1)} = \frac{0.2}{0.6} = \frac{1}{3}.$$

So the conditional p.m.f. is as follows.

x	0	3
$p(x|1)$	$\frac{2}{3}$	$\frac{1}{3}$

Solution 7.4

(a) The marginal distributions are as follows.

x	0	1
$p_X(x)$	0.5	0.5

y	0	1
$p_Y(y)$	0.6	0.4

Note that, for example,

$$p_X(0)\, p_Y(0) = 0.5 \times 0.6 = 0.3 = p(0,0).$$

In fact, $p(x, y) = p_X(x)\, p_Y(y)$ holds for each of the four cells. Hence X and Y are independent.

(b) The marginal distributions are as follows.

x	0	1
$p_X(x)$	0.5	0.5

y	0	1
$p_Y(y)$	0.6	0.4

Since $p(0,0) = 0.2$, but $p_X(0)\, p_Y(0) = 0.3$, it follows that X and Y are not independent.

(c) The marginal distributions are as follows.

x	0	1
$p_X(x)$	0.75	0.25

y	0	1
$p_Y(y)$	0.6	0.4

In this case, X and Y are independent.

The examples in parts (a) and (b) illustrate the fact that although for any joint distribution the marginal distributions are uniquely determined, the converse is *not* true: for any pair of marginal distributions, there are many possible joint distributions.

Solution 7.5

(a) Using the conditional distribution in the solution to Activity 7.2,

$$E(Y \mid X = 0) = 0 \times \tfrac{1}{6} + 1 \times \tfrac{2}{3} + 2 \times \tfrac{1}{6} = 1.$$

On average, Mary receives one email in a week when she does not send any emails.

(b) Using the conditional distribution in the solution to Activity 7.3,

$$E(X \mid Y = 1) = 0 \times \tfrac{2}{3} + 3 \times \tfrac{1}{3} = 1.$$

The average number of emails that Mary sends in a week when she receives one email is 1.

Solution 7.6

(a) The marginal distributions of X and Y are given below.

x	1	2
$p_X(x)$	0.35	0.65

y	0	1	2
$p_Y(y)$	0.25	0.35	0.4

(b) The conditional distribution of Y given $X = 1$ is as follows.

y	0	1	2
$p(y\mid 1)$	$\tfrac{1}{7}$	$\tfrac{4}{7}$	$\tfrac{2}{7}$

Therefore

$$E(Y \mid X = 1) = 0 \times \tfrac{1}{7} + 1 \times \tfrac{4}{7} + 2 \times \tfrac{2}{7} = \tfrac{8}{7} = 1\tfrac{1}{7}.$$

The conditional distribution of X given $Y = 2$ is given below.

x	1	2
$p(x\mid 2)$	$\tfrac{1}{4}$	$\tfrac{3}{4}$

Therefore

$$E(X \mid Y = 2) = 1 \times \tfrac{1}{4} + 2 \times \tfrac{3}{4} = 1\tfrac{3}{4}.$$

Solution 7.7

When integrating $f(x, y)$ with respect to x, y is treated as if it were a constant. So for $0 \le y \le 1$,

$$
\begin{aligned}
f_Y(y) &= \int_0^1 f(x, y)\, dx \\
&= \int_0^1 (x + y)\, dx \\
&= \left[\tfrac{1}{2}x^2 + xy \right]_0^1 \\
&= \tfrac{1}{2} + y.
\end{aligned}
$$

Solution 8.1

(a) $3^2 = 3 \times 3 = 9$

(b) $2^{-3} = \dfrac{1}{2^3} = \dfrac{1}{8}$

(c) $27^{1/3} = \sqrt[3]{27} = 3$

(d) $16^{3/4} = \left(\sqrt[4]{16} \right)^3 = 2^3 = 8$

(e) $25^{-1/2} = \dfrac{1}{25^{1/2}} = \dfrac{1}{\sqrt{25}} = \dfrac{1}{5}$

Solution 8.2

(a) $x^2 \times x^4 = x^{2+4} = x^6$

(b) $(x^3)^2 = x^{3 \times 2} = x^6$

(c) $x^8 / x^2 = x^{8-2} = x^6$

Solution 8.3

(a) $y = \log(6 \times 4/3) = \log 8.$

(b) $y = \log x^2 - \log(x + 1)^3$

$$= \log \left(\dfrac{x^2}{(x + 1)^3} \right).$$

(c) Since $8 = 2^3$,

$$\log 8 = \log 2^3 = 3 \log 2.$$

Therefore

$$\dfrac{\log 8}{\log 2} = \dfrac{3 \log 2}{\log 2} = 3.$$

(d) $e^{4x} \times (e^{-3x})^2 = e^{4x} \times e^{-6x}$

$$= e^{4x - 6x}$$

$$= e^{-2x}.$$

(e) First note that

$$y = \log s - \log(1 - s) - kt$$

$$= \log \left(\dfrac{s}{1 - s} \right) - kt.$$

Then

$$
\begin{aligned}
e^y &= e^{\log(s/(1-s)) - kt} \\
&= e^{\log(s/(1-s))} \times e^{-kt} \\
&= \dfrac{s}{1 - s} e^{-kt}.
\end{aligned}
$$

Solution 8.4

(a) $y = \log e^{3x} = 3x$

(b) $y = e^{\log(2x+3)} = 2x + 3$

(c) $y = e^{4\log((10-x)/10)}$

$= e^{\log(((10-x)/10)^4)}$

$= \left(\dfrac{10 - x}{10}\right)^4$

(d) $y = e^{-3\log(1+x)}$

$= e^{\log((1+x)^{-3})}$

$= (1 + x)^{-3}$

$= \dfrac{1}{(1 + x)^3}$

Solution 8.5

(a) Each term in S_1 is equal to the previous term multiplied by s^2. For $|s^2| < 1$,

$S_1 = 1 + s^2 + (s^2)^2 + (s^2)^3 + \cdots$

$= \dfrac{1}{1 - s^2}.$

(b) Each term in S_2 is equal to the previous term multiplied by $\frac{2}{3}s$. Provided that $-1 < \frac{2}{3}s < 1$,

$S_2 = 9s\left(1 + \frac{2}{3}s + \frac{4}{9}s^2 + \frac{8}{27}s^3 + \cdots\right)$

$= 9s \times \dfrac{1}{1 - \frac{2}{3}s}$

$= \dfrac{27s}{3 - 2s}.$

Solution 8.6

The function $U(s)$ is of the form $1/(1 - x)$ with $x = s^2 + 3s^3$, so provided that $|s^2 + 3s^3| < 1$,

$U(s) = 1 + (s^2 + 3s^3) + (s^2 + 3s^3)^2 + (s^2 + 3s^3)^3$

$\quad + \cdots$

$= 1 + s^2 + 3s^3 + s^4(1 + 3s)^2 + s^6(1 + 3s)^3 + \cdots$

$= 1 + s^2 + 3s^3 + s^4 + 6s^5 + 9s^6$

$\quad + s^6 + 9s^7 + 27s^8 + 27s^9 + \cdots$

$= 1 + s^2 + 3s^3 + s^4 + 6s^5 + 10s^6 + \cdots.$

Solution 8.7

(a) Since $h(x) = 7x^{-3}$,

$h'(x) = 7 \times -3x^{-4} = -\dfrac{21}{x^4}.$

(b) Using the quotient rule with $f(x) = 3x$ and $g(x) = 4 - x$,

$h'(x) = \dfrac{3(4 - x) - 3x \times (-1)}{(4 - x)^2}$

$= \dfrac{12}{(4 - x)^2}.$

(c) Since $h(x) = (5 - 2x)^{-3}$, using the composite rule,

$h'(x) = -3(5 - 2x)^{-4} \times (-2)$

$= \dfrac{6}{(5 - 2x)^4}.$

(d) Using the fact that the derivative of $\log g(x)$ is $g'(x)/g(x)$,

$h'(x) = \dfrac{-1}{1 - x} = -\dfrac{1}{1 - x}.$

Solution 8.8

(a) $\displaystyle\int 6x^2\, dx = 6\int x^2\, dx$

$= 6 \times \dfrac{x^3}{3} + c$

$= 2x^3 + c$

(b) $\displaystyle\int \dfrac{1}{3x^2}\, dx = \frac{1}{3}\int x^{-2}\, dx$

$= \frac{1}{3} \times \dfrac{x^{-1}}{-1} + c$

$= -\dfrac{1}{3x} + c$

(c) $\displaystyle\int \dfrac{1}{1 + x}\, dx = \log(1 + x) + c$

(d) $\displaystyle\int \dfrac{1}{1 - x}\, dx = -\int \dfrac{-1}{1 - x}\, dx$

$= -\log(1 - x) + c$

(e) $\displaystyle\int \dfrac{6}{2x + 3}\, dx = 3\int \dfrac{2}{2x + 3}\, dx$

$= 3\log(2x + 3) + c$

Solution 8.9

(a) $\displaystyle\int_1^2 \dfrac{16}{x^3}\, dx = 16\int_1^2 x^{-3}\, dx$

$= 16\left[\dfrac{x^{-2}}{-2}\right]_1^2$

$= \left[\dfrac{-8}{x^2}\right]_1^2$

$= -2 - (-8)$

$= 6$

(b) $\displaystyle\int_2^4 \dfrac{1}{1 + x}\, dx = \left[\log(1 + x)\right]_2^4$

$= \log 5 - \log 3$

$\simeq 0.511$

(c) $\displaystyle\int_0^2 \dfrac{6}{2x + 3}\, dx = \left[3\log(2x + 3)\right]_0^2$

$= 3\log 7 - 3\log 3$

$\simeq 2.542$

Solution 8.10

Integration by parts is used first with

$$f(x) = x^2, \quad g'(x) = e^{-3x}.$$

Then

$$f'(x) = 2x, \quad g(x) = -\tfrac{1}{3}e^{-3x}.$$

Using (8.2) and the fact that for $k > 0$ and any n, $x^n e^{-kx} \to 0$ as $x \to \infty$,

$$\int_0^\infty x^2 e^{-3x}\, dx = \left[x^2 \times -\tfrac{1}{3}e^{-3x}\right]_0^\infty$$

$$- \int_0^\infty 2x \times \left(-\tfrac{1}{3}e^{-3x}\right) dx$$

$$= 0 + \tfrac{2}{3}\int_0^\infty x e^{-3x}\, dx.$$

At this stage, the integral on the right-hand side must be found using integration by parts with $f(x) = x$ and $g'(x) = e^{-3x}$, as in Example 8.7. This gives

$$\int_0^\infty x^2 e^{-3x}\, dx = 0 + \tfrac{2}{3}\left[-\tfrac{1}{3}x e^{-3x} - \tfrac{1}{9}e^{-3x}\right]_0^\infty$$

$$= 0 + \tfrac{2}{3} \times \tfrac{1}{9}$$

$$= \tfrac{2}{27}.$$

Solution 8.11

The substitution $u = 1 - x$ gives

$$\frac{du}{dx} = -1.$$

Substituting u for $1 - x$, $1 - u$ for x, and $\dfrac{du}{dx}$ for -1 in the integrand gives

$$\int \frac{2x}{(1-x)^2}\, dx = \int \frac{2(1-u)}{u^2}\left(-\frac{du}{dx}\right) dx$$

$$= \int \frac{-2 + 2u}{u^2}\, du$$

$$= \int \left(-\frac{2}{u^2} + \frac{2}{u}\right) du$$

$$= \frac{2}{u} + 2\log u + c$$

$$= \frac{2}{1-x} + 2\log(1-x) + c.$$

Solution 8.12

The term $3x^2 y^2$ is of the form $f(x)\,g(y)$, where $f(x) = 3x^2$ and $g(y) = y^2$. Separating the variables gives

$$\frac{1}{y^2}\frac{dy}{dx} = 3x^2,$$

so

$$\int \frac{1}{y^2}\frac{dy}{dx}\, dx = \int 3x^2\, dx,$$

or

$$\int \frac{1}{y^2}\, dy = \int 3x^2\, dx.$$

Integrating both sides gives

$$-\frac{1}{y} = x^3 + c.$$

Since $y = 1$ when $x = 1$,

$$-1 = 1 + c,$$

so $c = -2$, and hence

$$-\frac{1}{y} = x^3 - 2.$$

Rearranging this equation gives

$$y = \frac{1}{2 - x^3}.$$

Solution 8.13

This differential equation is of the form in (8.3), with $h(x) = 2$ and $k(x) = 4x e^{-2x}$. Therefore

$$H(x) = \int 2\, dx = 2x,$$

and hence the integrating factor is e^{2x}. Multiplying both sides of the differential equation by the integrating factor gives

$$e^{2x}\frac{dy}{dx} + 2e^{2x}y = 4x,$$

or equivalently,

$$\frac{d}{dx}\left(e^{2x}y\right) = 4x.$$

Integrating both sides gives

$$e^{2x}y = \int 4x\, dx = 2x^2 + c,$$

where c is an arbitrary constant. Since $y = 0$ when $x = 0$,

$$0 = 0 + c,$$

so $c = 0$ and hence

$$y = 2x^2 e^{-2x}.$$

Solutions to Exercises

Solution 1.1

(a) Using (1.1) gives
$$P(\overline{A}) = 1 - P(A) = 0.7.$$

(b) $P(\overline{B}) = 1 - P(B) = 0.4.$

(c) Using (1.3) gives
$$P(A \cup B) = P(A) + P(B) - P(A \cap B)$$
$$= 0.3 + 0.6 - 0.2$$
$$= 0.7.$$

(d) Since $\overline{A} \cap \overline{B}$ is the complement of $A \cup B$,
$$P(\overline{A} \cap \overline{B}) = P(\overline{A \cup B}) = 1 - P(A \cup B) = 0.3.$$

(e) The shaded area in Figure S.5 represents the event $\overline{A} \cap B$.

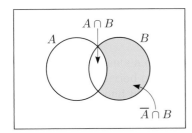

Figure S.5 The event $\overline{A} \cap B$

Hence
$$P(\overline{A} \cap B) = P(B) - P(A \cap B) = 0.6 - 0.2 = 0.4.$$

Solution 1.2

(a) $P(A \cap B) = P(A|B) P(B) = 0.65 \times 0.4 = 0.26.$

(b) $P(\overline{B}) = 1 - P(B) = 0.6$ so, by the Theorem of Total Probability,
$$P(A) = P(A|B) P(B) + P(A|\overline{B}) P(\overline{B})$$
$$= 0.65 \times 0.4 + 0.35 \times 0.6$$
$$= 0.47.$$

(c) $P(A \cup B) = P(A) + P(B) - P(A \cap B)$
$$= 0.47 + 0.4 - 0.26$$
$$= 0.61.$$

Solution 1.3

(a) $P(A \cap B) = P(B|A) P(A) = 0.4 \times 0.5 = 0.2.$

(b) $P(A \cup B) = P(A) + P(B) - P(A \cap B)$, so
$$P(B) = P(A \cup B) + P(A \cap B) - P(A)$$
$$= 0.9 + 0.2 - 0.5$$
$$= 0.6.$$

(c) $P(A|B) = \dfrac{P(A \cap B)}{P(B)} = \dfrac{0.2}{0.6} = \frac{1}{3}.$

Solution 1.4

(a) Let D be the event that an item is defective, and let M_1 and M_2 be the events that an item comes from machines 1 and 2, respectively. Then
$$P(M_1) = 0.6, \quad P(M_2) = 0.4,$$
$$P(D|M_1) = 0.02, \quad P(D|M_2) = 0.05.$$

(b) The probability required is $P(D)$. By the Theorem of Total Probability,
$$P(D) = P(D|M_1) P(M_1) + P(D|M_2) P(M_2)$$
$$= 0.02 \times 0.6 + 0.05 \times 0.4$$
$$= 0.032.$$

(c) The probability required is $P(M_1|D)$. Using Bayes' formula,
$$P(M_1|D) = \frac{P(D|M_1) P(M_1)}{P(D)} = \frac{0.02 \times 0.6}{0.032} = 0.375.$$

Solution 2.1

(a) $\dbinom{6}{1} = \dfrac{6!}{1! \, 5!} = \dfrac{1 \times 2 \times 3 \times 4 \times 5 \times 6}{(1)(1 \times 2 \times 3 \times 4 \times 5)} = 6$

(b) $\dbinom{7}{2} = \dfrac{7!}{2! \, 5!} = \dfrac{1 \times 2 \times \cdots \times 5 \times 6 \times 7}{(1 \times 2)(1 \times 2 \times \cdots \times 5)}$
$$= \frac{6 \times 7}{1 \times 2} = 21$$

(c) $\dbinom{11}{9} = \dfrac{11!}{9! \, 2!} = \dfrac{1 \times 2 \times \cdots \times 9 \times 10 \times 11}{(1 \times 2 \times \cdots \times 9)(1 \times 2)}$
$$= \frac{10 \times 11}{1 \times 2} = 55$$

(d) $\dbinom{9}{6} = \dfrac{9!}{6! \, 3!} = \dfrac{1 \times 2 \times \cdots \times 6 \times 7 \times 8 \times 9}{(1 \times 2 \times \cdots \times 6)(1 \times 2 \times 3)}$
$$= \frac{7 \times 8 \times 9}{1 \times 2 \times 3} = 84$$

Solution 2.2

(a) $P(X = 2) = \dbinom{6}{2} 0.6^2 0.4^4$
$$= 15 \times 0.6^2 \times 0.4^4$$
$$= 0.138\,24$$
$$\simeq 0.1382$$

(b) $P(Y < 3) = P(Y = 0) + P(Y = 1) + P(Y = 2)$
$$\simeq 0.2097 + 0.3670 + 0.2753$$
$$= 0.8520$$

(c) $P(Z > 8) = P(Z = 9) + P(Z = 10)$
$$\simeq 0.3874 + 0.3487$$
$$= 0.7361$$

Solution 2.3

(a) $P(X = 4) = \dfrac{e^{-1.8}1.8^4}{4!} \simeq 0.0723$

(b) $P(Y \geq 3) = 1 - (P(Y = 0) + P(Y = 1)$
$$+ P(Y = 2))$$
$$\simeq 1 - (0.0183 + 0.0733 + 0.1465)$$
$$= 1 - 0.2381$$
$$= 0.7619$$

Solution 2.4

Since n is large and p is small, a Poisson distribution can be used to approximate the binomial distribution:
$$X \approx \text{Poisson}(300 \times 0.02) = \text{Poisson}(6).$$
Hence
$$P(X \leq 3) = P(X = 0) + P(X = 1) + P(X = 2)$$
$$+ P(X = 3)$$
$$\simeq e^{-6} + \frac{e^{-6}6}{1!} + \frac{e^{-6}6^2}{2!} + \frac{e^{-6}6^3}{3!}$$
$$\simeq 0.1512.$$

Solution 2.5

(a) $A \sim B(6, 0.03)$, $B \sim G_1(0.03)$ and C has a negative binomial distribution with parameters 3 and 0.03, and range $\{0, 1, \ldots\}$.

(b) $D \sim B(150, 0.03)$, so since n is large and p is small, Poisson's approximation for rare events can be used:
$$D \approx \text{Poisson}(150 \times 0.03) = \text{Poisson}(4.5).$$

Solution 2.6

(a) Using (2.3),
$$E(X) = 0 \times 0.4 + 1 \times 0.2 + 2 \times 0.3 + 3 \times 0.1$$
$$= 1.1.$$
Using (2.8) to find the variance:
$$E(X^2) = 0^2 \times 0.4 + 1^2 \times 0.2 + 2^2 \times 0.3 + 3^2 \times 0.1$$
$$= 2.3,$$
$$V(X) = 2.3 - 1.1^2 = 1.09.$$

(b) Values of the c.d.f. of Y are given in the table below.

y	0	1	2	3	4
$F(y)$	0	0.5	0.8	0.9	1

Using (2.4), the expected value of Y is
$$E(Y) = (1 - 0) + (1 - 0.5) + (1 - 0.8) + (1 - 0.9)$$
$$+ (1 - 1) + 0 + \cdots$$
$$= 1 + 0.5 + 0.2 + 0.1$$
$$= 1.8.$$

Solution 3.1

The p.g.f.s in parts (a), (b) and (c) can be written down using either Table 3.4 or the table of discrete probability distributions in the *Handbook* (Table 8).

(a) $\Pi(s) = (0.4 + 0.6s)^{10}$

(b) $\Pi(s) = \dfrac{0.3}{1 - 0.7s}$

(c) $\Pi(s) = \left(\dfrac{\frac{5}{8}s}{1 - \frac{3}{8}s}\right)^3 = \left(\dfrac{5s}{8 - 3s}\right)^3$

(d) $\Pi(s) = s^5$

Solution 3.2

(a) The p.g.f. can be written as
$$\Pi(s) = \frac{\frac{5}{7}}{1 - \frac{2}{7}s},$$
so $X \sim G_0\left(\frac{2}{7}\right)$ and
$$E(X) = \frac{p}{q} = \frac{2}{5} = 0.4,$$
$$V(X) = \frac{p}{q^2} = \frac{14}{25} = 0.56.$$

(b) The p.g.f. can be written as
$$\Pi(s) = \frac{\frac{5}{7}s}{1 - \frac{2}{7}s},$$
so $X \sim G_1\left(\frac{5}{7}\right)$ and
$$E(X) = \frac{1}{p} = 1.4, \quad V(X) = \frac{q}{p^2} = 0.56.$$

(c) The p.g.f. can be written as
$$\Pi(s) = \left(\frac{\frac{2}{7}}{1 - \frac{5}{7}s}\right)^2,$$
so X has a negative binomial distribution with parameters $r = 2$, $p = \frac{5}{7}$ and range $\{0, 1, \ldots\}$. Hence
$$E(X) = \frac{rp}{q} = 5, \quad V(X) = \frac{rp}{q^2} = 17.5.$$

(d) The p.g.f. can be written as
$$\Pi(s) = \left(\frac{\frac{2}{7}s}{1 - \frac{5}{7}s}\right)^3,$$
so X has a negative binomial distribution with parameters $r = 3$, $p = \frac{2}{7}$ and range $\{3, 4, \ldots\}$. Hence
$$E(X) = \frac{r}{p} = 10.5, \quad V(X) = \frac{rq}{p^2} = 26.25.$$

(e) The p.g.f. can be written as $(0.9 + 0.1s)^7$, so $X \sim B(7, 0.1)$. Hence $E(X) = 0.7$ and $V(X) = 0.63$.

(f) The p.g.f. can be written as $e^{-\frac{3}{4}(1-s)}$, so $X \sim \text{Poisson}\left(\frac{3}{4}\right)$. Hence $E(X) = \frac{3}{4}$ and $V(X) = \frac{3}{4}$.

Solution 3.3

(a) (i) $P(X = 0) = \Pi(0) = \frac{4}{5}$.

(ii) $\Pi'(s) = \dfrac{8s}{(5 - s^2)^2}$, so

$$E(X) = \Pi'(1) = \tfrac{1}{2}.$$

(iii) $\Pi''(s) = \dfrac{40 + 24s^2}{(5 - s^2)^3}$, so $\Pi''(1) = 1$ and hence

$$V(X) = \Pi''(1) + \mu - \mu^2$$
$$= 1 + \tfrac{1}{2} - \tfrac{1}{4}$$
$$= 1\tfrac{1}{4}.$$

(b) The p.g.f. can be written as

$$\Pi(s) = \dfrac{0.8}{1 - 0.2s^2}.$$

Since $\dfrac{1}{1 - x} = 1 + x + x^2 + \cdots$ for $|x| \le 1$,

$$\Pi(s) = 0.8(1 + 0.2s^2 + (0.2s^2)^2 + \cdots)$$
$$= 0.8(1 + 0.2s^2 + 0.04s^4 + \cdots)$$
$$= 0.8 + 0.16s^2 + 0.032s^4 + \cdots.$$

Hence the range of X is $\{0, 2, 4, \ldots\}$, and $p(0) = 0.8$, $p(1) = 0$, $p(2) = 0.16$, $p(3) = 0$, $p(4) = 0.032$.

Solution 3.4

(a) (i) Using (3.7),

$$\Pi_U(s) = \Pi_X(s)\,\Pi_Y(s) = \tfrac{1}{4}(1 + s)^2 e^{-2(1-s)}.$$

(ii) Using (3.9),

$$\Pi_V(s) = \Pi_X(s^2) = \tfrac{1}{4}(1 + s^2)^2.$$

That is, the p.g.f. of $V = 2X$ is obtained by replacing s by s^2 in the p.g.f. of X.

(iii) Using (3.9),

$$\Pi_W(s) = \Pi_Y(s^3) = e^{-2(1-s^3)}.$$

(b) $\Pi_Z(s) = \tfrac{1}{81}s^2(2 + s)^4 = s^2 \times \left(\tfrac{2}{3} + \tfrac{1}{3}s\right)^4$.

Since s^2 is the p.g.f. of a degenerate random variable that takes the value 2, and $\left(\tfrac{2}{3} + \tfrac{1}{3}s\right)^4$ is the p.g.f. of $X \sim B\left(4, \tfrac{1}{3}\right)$,

$$Z = 2 + X, \quad \text{where } X \sim B\left(4, \tfrac{1}{3}\right).$$

Solution 4.1

(a) $P(X < 0.4) = F(0.4) = 0.04$,

$$P(0.6 < X < 1.4) = P(X < 1.4) - P(X \le 0.6)$$
$$= P(X \le 1.4) - P(X \le 0.6)$$
$$= F(1.4) - F(0.6)$$
$$= 0.49 - 0.09$$
$$= 0.4,$$

$$P(X > 1.6) = 1 - P(X \le 1.6)$$
$$= 1 - F(1.6)$$
$$= 1 - 0.64$$
$$= 0.36.$$

(b) The p.d.f. of X is

$$f(x) = \begin{cases} \tfrac{1}{2}x, & 0 \le x \le 2, \\ 0, & \text{otherwise.} \end{cases}$$

(c) The mean of X is

$$E(X) = \int_{-\infty}^{\infty} x\,f(x)\,dx$$
$$= \int_0^2 \tfrac{1}{2}x^2\,dx$$
$$= \left[\dfrac{x^3}{6}\right]_0^2$$
$$= \tfrac{4}{3}.$$

Similarly,

$$E(X^2) = \int_{-\infty}^{\infty} x^2\,f(x)\,dx = \int_0^2 \tfrac{1}{2}x^3\,dx = 2,$$

so

$$V(X) = E(X^2) - \mu^2 = 2 - \left(\tfrac{4}{3}\right)^2 = \tfrac{2}{9}.$$

(d) The median m satisfies $F(m) = \tfrac{1}{2}$, so

$$\tfrac{1}{4}m^2 = \tfrac{1}{2}.$$

Therefore

$$m = \sqrt{2} \simeq 1.414.$$

(e) The 0.9-quantile, $q_{0.9}$, is the solution of

$$F(q_{0.9}) = \tfrac{1}{4}q_{0.9}^2 = 0.9,$$

so

$$q_{0.9}^2 = 3.6,$$

and hence

$$q_{0.9} = \sqrt{3.6} \simeq 1.897.$$

Solution 4.2

(a) $P(X < 3) = \displaystyle\int_2^3 \tfrac{1}{2}(x - 2)\,dx$

$$= \tfrac{1}{2}\left[\tfrac{1}{2}x^2 - 2x\right]_2^3$$
$$= \tfrac{1}{4}.$$

(b) The mean of X is

$$E(X) = \int_{-\infty}^{\infty} x\,f(x)\,dx$$
$$= \tfrac{1}{2}\int_2^4 (x^2 - 2x)\,dx$$
$$= \tfrac{1}{2}\left[\tfrac{1}{3}x^3 - x^2\right]_2^4$$
$$= 3\tfrac{1}{3}.$$

Similarly,

$$E(X^2) = \tfrac{1}{2}\int_2^4 (x^3 - 2x^2)\,dx$$
$$= \tfrac{1}{2}\left[\tfrac{1}{4}x^4 - \tfrac{2}{3}x^3\right]_2^4$$
$$= 11\tfrac{1}{3},$$

so

$$V(X) = E(X^2) - \mu^2 = 11\tfrac{1}{3} - \left(3\tfrac{1}{3}\right)^2 = \tfrac{2}{9}.$$

(c) For $x < 2$, $F(x) = 0$, and for $x > 4$, $F(x) = 1$. For $2 \le x \le 4$,

$$F(x) = P(X \le x)$$
$$= \int_{-\infty}^{x} f(u)\,du$$
$$= \int_{2}^{x} \tfrac{1}{2}(u - 2)\,du$$
$$= \left[\tfrac{1}{4}u^2 - u\right]_{2}^{x}$$
$$= \tfrac{1}{4}x^2 - x + 1.$$

(d) Using (4.4), the expected value of X is obtained as follows:

$$E(X) = \int_{0}^{\infty} (1 - F(x))\,dx$$
$$= \int_{0}^{2} 1\,dx + \int_{2}^{4}\left(1 - \left(\tfrac{1}{4}x^2 - x + 1\right)\right)dx$$
$$\quad + \int_{4}^{\infty} 0\,dx$$
$$= 2 + \int_{2}^{4}\left(x - \tfrac{1}{4}x^2\right)dx + 0$$
$$= 2 + \left[\tfrac{1}{2}x^2 - \tfrac{1}{12}x^3\right]_{2}^{4}$$
$$= 2 + \tfrac{4}{3}$$
$$= 3\tfrac{1}{3}.$$

(e) The median m is the solution of $F(x) = \tfrac{1}{2}$, that is, of

$$\tfrac{1}{4}x^2 - x + 1 = \tfrac{1}{2}$$

or

$$x^2 - 4x + 2 = 0.$$

This equation has solutions

$$x = \frac{4 \pm \sqrt{16 - 8}}{2} = 2 \pm \sqrt{2}.$$

Since X takes values between 2 and 4, the median is

$$m = 2 + \sqrt{2} \simeq 3.414.$$

Solution 5.1

(a) The service times of the two assistants have exponential distributions: $T_1 \sim M\left(\tfrac{1}{2}\right)$, $T_2 \sim M\left(\tfrac{1}{3}\right)$. By the memoryless property, these are also the distributions of the times remaining until they are free to serve a new customer. The time T that I will have to wait before one of the assistants is free is the minimum of T_1 and T_2, so

$$T \sim M\left(\tfrac{1}{2} + \tfrac{1}{3}\right) = M\left(\tfrac{5}{6}\right).$$

The probability that I will have to wait more than 2 minutes is

$$P(T > 2) = e^{-\frac{5}{6} \times 2} = e^{-5/3} \simeq 0.189.$$

(b) The mean and standard deviation of $M(\lambda)$ are both equal to $1/\lambda$, so

$$E(T) = \frac{1}{5/6} = 1.2 \text{ minutes},$$

and the standard deviation of T is also 1.2 minutes (or 72 seconds).

Solution 5.2

(a) By the memoryless property, the distribution of the time T_1 until the service of the customer currently being served is completed is $M\left(\tfrac{1}{2}\right)$. The distributions of the service times T_2 and T_3 are also $M\left(\tfrac{1}{2}\right)$. Since T_1, T_2 and T_3 are independent, the distribution of their sum W, the time that I will have to wait, is $\Gamma\left(3, \tfrac{1}{2}\right)$.

(b) The mean and variance of $\Gamma(n, \lambda)$ are n/λ and n/λ^2, respectively, so

$$E(W) = \frac{3}{1/2} = 6 \text{ minutes},$$

$$V(W) = \frac{3}{(1/2)^2} = 12 \text{ (minutes)}^2,$$

and hence the standard deviation of W is $\sqrt{12} \simeq 3.46$ minutes.

Solution 5.3

(a) By the central limit theorem,

$$\overline{X} \approx N\left(3, \tfrac{10}{160}\right) = N\left(3, \tfrac{1}{16}\right).$$

(b) $T \approx N(160 \times 3, 160 \times 10) = N(480, 1600)$.

(c) The probability required is

$$P(T < 400) \simeq P\left(Z < \frac{400 - 480}{\sqrt{1600}}\right)$$
$$= P(Z < -2)$$
$$= \Phi(-2)$$
$$= 1 - \Phi(2)$$
$$= 1 - 0.9772$$
$$= 0.0228 \simeq 0.023.$$

Solution 6.1

The simulated values are solutions of

$$F(x) = 1 - \frac{1}{x^3} = u.$$

Given $u_1 = 0.147\,12$, x_1 is the solution of

$$1 - \frac{1}{x_1^3} = 0.147\,12,$$

so

$$x_1 = \frac{1}{(0.852\,88)^{1/3}} \simeq 1.054.$$

Similarly, $u_2 = 0.064\,02$ and $u_3 = 0.949\,37$ give

$$x_2 \simeq 1.022, \quad x_3 \simeq 2.703.$$

Solution 6.2

By the memoryless property of the exponential distribution, the time in minutes after 9 am at which the first car passes is exponentially distributed with mean 4, so three simulated values from $M\left(\frac{1}{4}\right)$ are required. These are obtained by multiplying numbers from Table 6 in the *Handbook* by 4. Using numbers from the fourth row gives the following results.

Number	1.7001	0.3986	0.7155
Simulated time	6.8004	1.5944	2.8620
Total time	6.8004	8.3948	11.2568

In this simulation, the first three cars pass at approximately 9.07 am, 9.08 am and 9.11 am.

Solution 6.3

Since $\mu = 6$ and $\sigma = \sqrt{25} = 5$, for each number z from the table, the simulated value is $x = 5z + 6$. The three simulated observations from $N(6, 25)$ are

$$x_1 = 5 \times -0.5049 + 6 = 3.4755 \simeq 3.476,$$
$$x_2 = 5 \times 1.4433 + 6 = 13.2165 \simeq 13.217,$$
$$x_3 = 5 \times 0.2410 + 6 = 7.205.$$

Solution 6.4

(a) One possible scheme using pairs of digits is given in Table S.4.

Table S.4   A simulation scheme

Digits	Outcome
01, ..., 52	Boy
53, ..., 99, 00	Girl

(b) Using digits from the twentieth row of Table 5 in the *Handbook* gives the following results.

Digits	80	74	95	27	74
Outcome	Girl	Girl	Girl	Boy	Girl

Solution 6.5

(a) Values of the p.m.f. and c.d.f. of $X \sim B(9, 0.3)$ are given in Table S.5.

Table S.5   Values of the p.m.f. and c.d.f. of X

x	0	1	2	3	4	$\cdots$
$p(x)$	0.0404	0.1556	0.2668	0.2668	0.1715	$\cdots$
$F(x)$	0.0404	0.1960	0.4628	0.7296	0.9011	$\cdots$

Given $u = 0.7423$,
$$F(3) < u \le F(4),$$
so the simulated value is $x = 4$.

(b) Values of the p.m.f. and c.d.f. of $X \sim \text{Poisson}(2.5)$ are given in Table S.6.

Table S.6   Values of the p.m.f. and c.d.f. of X

x	0	1	2	$\cdots$
$p(x)$	0.0821	0.2052	0.2565	$\cdots$
$F(x)$	0.0821	0.2873	0.5438	$\cdots$

Given $u = 0.3817$,
$$F(1) < u \le F(2),$$
so the simulated value is $x = 2$.

Solution 7.1

(a) The completed table is given below.

		y			
		1	2	3	$p_X(x)$
x	0	0.1	0.2	0.3	0.6
	1	0.2	0.1	0.1	0.4
$p_Y(y)$		0.3	0.3	0.4	

(b) By definition, $p(y|1) = p(1, y)/p_X(1)$, so the conditional distribution of Y given $X = 1$ is as follows.

y	1	2	3
$p(y|1)$	0.5	0.25	0.25

Therefore
$$E(Y \mid X = 1) = 1 \times 0.5 + 2 \times 0.25 + 3 \times 0.25$$
$$= 1.75.$$

Solution 7.2

(a) The completed table is given below.

		y			
		0	1	2	$p_X(x)$
x	0	$\frac{1}{8}$	0	$\frac{1}{3}$	$\frac{11}{24}$
	1	$\frac{1}{6}$	$\frac{3}{8}$	0	$\frac{13}{24}$
$p_Y(y)$		$\frac{7}{24}$	$\frac{3}{8}$	$\frac{1}{3}$	

(b) The conditional p.m.f. of X given $Y = 0$ is obtained using $p(x|0) = p(x, 0)/p_Y(0)$. The p.m.f. is as follows.

x	0	1
$p(x|0)$	$\frac{3}{7}$	$\frac{4}{7}$

Therefore
$$E(X \mid Y = 0) = 0 \times \frac{3}{7} + 1 \times \frac{4}{7} = \frac{4}{7}.$$

Solution 8.1

(a) $3^3 = 3 \times 3 \times 3 = 27$

(b) $3^{-2} = \dfrac{1}{3^2} = \frac{1}{9}$

(c) $27^{2/3} = \left(\sqrt[3]{27}\right)^2 = 3^2 = 9$

(d) $64^{-1/3} = \dfrac{1}{\sqrt[3]{64}} = \frac{1}{4}$

Solution 8.2

(a) $x^3 \times x = x^3 \times x^1 = x^{3+1} = x^4$

(b) $(x^4)^3 = x^{4 \times 3} = x^{12}$

(c) $x^{12}/x^4 = x^{12-4} = x^8$

Solution 8.3

(a) $y = 2\log 10 - \log 20 + \log 2$

$ = \log 10^2 - \log 20 + \log 2$

$ = \log\left(\dfrac{10^2}{20} \times 2\right)$

$ = \log 10.$

(b) $\dfrac{\log 27}{\log 9} = \dfrac{\log 3^3}{\log 3^2}$

$\phantom{\dfrac{\log 27}{\log 9}} = \dfrac{3\log 3}{2\log 3}$

$\phantom{\dfrac{\log 27}{\log 9}} = \frac{3}{2}.$

(c) $\dfrac{e^{4t} \times (e^{-3t})^2}{e^{-5t}} = \dfrac{e^{4t} \times e^{-6t}}{e^{-5t}}$

$\phantom{\dfrac{e^{4t} \times (e^{-3t})^2}{e^{-5t}}} = e^{4t-6t-(-5t)}$

$\phantom{\dfrac{e^{4t} \times (e^{-3t})^2}{e^{-5t}}} = e^{3t}.$

(d) (i) Since $\log(e^{x-2}) = x - 2$,

$y = 3\log(e^{x-2}) = 3(x - 2).$

(ii) Since $-4\log(x + 2) = \log((x+2)^{-4})$,

$y = e^{-4\log(x+2)}$

$ = e^{\log((x+2)^{-4})}$

$ = (x + 2)^{-4}$

$ = \dfrac{1}{(x+2)^4}.$

Solution 8.4

(a) Since $h(x) = 8x^{-2}$,

$$h'(x) = 8 \times -2x^{-3} = -\dfrac{16}{x^3}.$$

(b) The quotient rule should be used with

$$f(x) = 2 + x, \quad g(x) = 5 - 2x,$$

so that

$$f'(x) = 1, \quad g'(x) = -2.$$

Then

$$h'(x) = \dfrac{1 \times (5 - 2x) - (2 + x) \times (-2)}{(5 - 2x)^2}$$

$$ = \dfrac{5 - 2x + 4 + 2x}{(5 - 2x)^2}$$

$$ = \dfrac{9}{(5 - 2x)^2}.$$

(c) Since $h(x)$ is of the form $\log g(x)$ with $g(x) = 2x + 3$,

$$h'(x) = \dfrac{g'(x)}{g(x)} = \dfrac{2}{2x + 3}.$$

Solution 8.5

(a) $\displaystyle \int \dfrac{18}{x^4}\, dx = \int 18x^{-4}\, dx$

$\phantom{\int \dfrac{18}{x^4}\, dx} = 18 \times \dfrac{x^{-3}}{-3} + c$

$\phantom{\int \dfrac{18}{x^4}\, dx} = -\dfrac{6}{x^3} + c.$

(b) Using the integral found in part (a),

$$\int_1^2 \dfrac{18}{x^4}\, dx = \left[-\dfrac{6}{x^3}\right]_1^2$$

$$\phantom{\int_1^2 \dfrac{18}{x^4}\, dx} = -\tfrac{6}{8} - (-6)$$

$$\phantom{\int_1^2 \dfrac{18}{x^4}\, dx} = 5\tfrac{1}{4}.$$

(c) $\displaystyle \int \left(\dfrac{1}{x} - \dfrac{1}{1 - x}\right) dx = \log x + \log(1 - x) + c.$

(d) Integration by parts can be used with

$$f(x) = x, \quad g'(x) = e^{-2x},$$

so

$$f'(x) = 1, \quad g(x) = -\tfrac{1}{2}e^{-2x}.$$

Then

$$\int_0^\infty xe^{-2x}\, dx = \left[-\tfrac{1}{2}xe^{-2x}\right]_0^\infty - \int_0^\infty -\tfrac{1}{2}e^{-2x}\, dx$$

$$\phantom{\int_0^\infty xe^{-2x}\, dx} = 0 + \int_0^\infty \tfrac{1}{2}e^{-2x}\, dx$$

$$\phantom{\int_0^\infty xe^{-2x}\, dx} = \left[-\tfrac{1}{4}e^{-2x}\right]_0^\infty$$

$$\phantom{\int_0^\infty xe^{-2x}\, dx} = 0 - \left(-\tfrac{1}{4}\right)$$

$$\phantom{\int_0^\infty xe^{-2x}\, dx} = \tfrac{1}{4}.$$

Solution 8.6

(a) Separation of variables can be used with $f(x) = 5$ and $g(y) = y$. This gives

$$\int \frac{1}{y} \frac{dy}{dx} \, dx = \int 5 \, dx,$$

or

$$\int \frac{1}{y} \, dy = \int 5 \, dx,$$

so

$$\log y = 5x + c,$$

where c is an arbitrary constant. Since $y = 1$ when $x = 0$,

$$\log 1 = 0 + c,$$

and hence $c = 0$ (since $\log 1 = 0$). Therefore

$$\log y = 5x,$$

which gives

$$y = e^{5x}.$$

(b) The integrating factor method is required with $h(x) = 4$, so that

$$H(x) = \int 4 \, dx = 4x.$$

The integrating factor $e^{H(x)}$ is e^{4x}, so multiplying the differential equation throughout by e^{4x} gives

$$e^{4x} \frac{dy}{dx} + 4e^{4x} y = 2e^{-x} \times e^{4x}.$$

That is,

$$\frac{d}{dx}\left(e^{4x} y\right) = 2e^{3x}.$$

Integrating both sides gives

$$e^{4x} y = \tfrac{2}{3} e^{3x} + c.$$

Dividing through by e^{4x} gives

$$y = \tfrac{2}{3} e^{-x} + c e^{-4x}.$$

Since $y = 0$ when $x = 0$,

$$0 = \tfrac{2}{3} + c,$$

so

$$c = -\tfrac{2}{3},$$

and hence

$$y = \tfrac{2}{3}\left(e^{-x} - e^{-4x}\right).$$

Solution 9.1

This exercise covers some of the ideas and techniques discussed in Section 1.

(a) Let F, A, B, C be the events that Monica travels to work on foot, by bicycle, by bus and by car, respectively. Then

$$P(F) = 0.1, \ P(A) = 0.3, \ P(B) = 0.2, \ P(C) = 0.4.$$

If L is the event that she is late, then

$$P(L|F) = 0.35, \quad P(L|A) = 0.1,$$
$$P(L|B) = 0.4, \quad P(L|C) = 0.15.$$

(b) Since F, A, B, C are mutually exclusive and exhaustive events, by the Theorem of Total Probability,

$$\begin{aligned}
P(L) &= P(L|F)\,P(F) + P(L|A)\,P(A) \\
&\quad + P(L|B)\,P(B) + P(L|C)\,P(C) \\
&= 0.35 \times 0.1 + 0.1 \times 0.3 \\
&\quad + 0.4 \times 0.2 + 0.15 \times 0.4 \\
&= 0.205.
\end{aligned}$$

(c) By Bayes' formula,

$$P(F|L) = \frac{P(L|F)\,P(F)}{P(L)} = \frac{0.35 \times 0.1}{0.205} \simeq 0.171.$$

(d) By Bayes' formula,

$$P(F|\overline{L}) = \frac{P(\overline{L}|F)\,P(F)}{P(\overline{L})} = \frac{0.65 \times 0.1}{0.795} \simeq 0.082.$$

(e) By the Theorem of Total Probability,

$$P(L) = P(L|C)\,P(C) + P(L|\overline{C})\,P(\overline{C}).$$

That is,

$$0.205 = 0.15 \times 0.4 + P(L|\overline{C}) \times 0.6.$$

Therefore

$$P(L|\overline{C}) = \frac{0.205 - 0.06}{0.6} \simeq 0.242.$$

Solution 9.2

This exercise covers some of the ideas and techniques discussed in Section 1.

(a) The required probability is $P(T)$. By the Theorem of Total Probability,

$$\begin{aligned}
P(T) &= \sum_{i=1}^{3} P(T|D_i)\,P(D_i) \\
&= 0.21 \times 0.62 + 0.83 \times 0.27 + 0.68 \times 0.11 \\
&= 0.4291.
\end{aligned}$$

(b) Using Bayes' formula,

$$\begin{aligned}
P(D_1|T) &= \frac{P(T|D_1)\,P(D_1)}{P(T)} \\
&= \frac{0.21 \times 0.62}{0.4291} \\
&\simeq 0.303.
\end{aligned}$$

The probability that a patient who shows a positive reaction suffers from disease 1 is 0.303.

Similarly,

$$P(D_2|T) = \frac{0.83 \times 0.27}{0.4291} \simeq 0.522$$

and

$$P(D_3|T) \simeq 0.174.$$

As a check, $0.303 + 0.522 + 0.174 = 0.999 \simeq 1$. The discrepancy between 0.999 and 1 is due to rounding error.

Solution 9.3

This exercise covers some of the ideas and techniques discussed in Sections 1 and 2.

(a) The probability required is $P(X < 2)$, where $X \sim B(12, 0.03)$:
$$P(X < 2) = P(X = 0) + P(X = 1)$$
$$\simeq 0.6938 + 0.2575$$
$$= 0.9513.$$

(Retaining full calculator accuracy leads to 0.9514 to four decimal places.)

(b) The probability required is $P(Y = 0)$, where $Y \sim B(20, 0.03)$:
$$P(Y = 0) = (0.97)^{20} \simeq 0.5438.$$

(c) The exact probability is $P(Z = 4)$, where $Z \sim B(100, 0.03)$. An approximate distribution for Z is $\text{Poisson}(100 \times 0.03) = \text{Poisson}(3)$, so
$$P(Z = 4) \simeq \frac{e^{-3} 3^4}{4!} \simeq 0.1680.$$

(d) If R_A, R_B are the numbers in hospitals A and B who recover, then $R_A \sim B(n, p)$, so
$$P(R_A = r) = \binom{n}{r} p^r q^{n-r}, \quad \text{where } q = 1 - p.$$

(e) The total number of patients who recover is $R_A + R_B \sim B(m + n, p)$, so
$$P(R_A + R_B = k) = \binom{m + n}{k} p^k q^{m+n-k}.$$

(f) The probability required is
$$P(R_A = r \mid R_A + R_B = k)$$
$$= \frac{P(R_A + R_B = k \mid R_A = r)\, P(R_A = r)}{P(R_A + R_B = k)}$$
$$\text{(using Bayes' formula)}$$
$$= \frac{P(R_B = k - r)\, P(R_A = r)}{P(R_A + R_B = k)}$$
$$= \frac{\binom{m}{k-r} p^{k-r} q^{m-k+r} \binom{n}{r} p^r q^{n-r}}{\binom{m+n}{k} p^k q^{m+n-k}}$$
$$= \frac{\binom{m}{k-r} \binom{n}{r}}{\binom{m+n}{k}}.$$

Solution 9.4

This exercise covers some of the ideas and techniques discussed in Section 2.

(a) The number of successful kicks has a binomial distribution: $X \sim B(10, 0.96)$.

(i) $P(X = 8) = \binom{10}{8} 0.96^8\, 0.04^2 \simeq 0.0519.$

(ii) $P(X \geq 8) = P(X = 8) + P(X = 9) + P(X = 10)$
$$\simeq 0.0519 + 0.2770 + 0.6648$$
$$= 0.9937.$$

(Retaining full calculator accuracy throughout leads to 0.9938 to four decimal places.)

(b) The number of successful kicks is $X \sim B(10, p)$, where $p = 0.024(60 - y)$. Since
$$P(X \geq 1) = 0.99,$$
it follows that
$$P(X = 0) = q^{10} = 0.01.$$
Hence
$$p = 1 - q = 1 - (0.01)^{1/10} \simeq 0.3690.$$
Therefore
$$0.024(60 - y) \simeq 0.3690,$$
giving
$$y \simeq 44.62 \simeq 45 \text{ metres.}$$

(c) The number of kicks until he has his first success is $Y \sim G_1(p)$, where $p = 0.024(60 - 40) = 0.48$, so
$$P(Y \geq 3) = q^2 = 0.52^2 = 0.2704 \quad \text{(using (2.2)).}$$

(d) If Z is the number of kicks until he has two successes, then Z is negative binomial with parameters $r = 2$, $p = 0.48$ and range $\{2, 3, \ldots\}$. So
$$E(Z) = \frac{r}{p} = \frac{2}{0.48} \simeq 4.167.$$

Solution 9.5

This exercise covers some of the ideas and techniques discussed in Section 2.

(a) Since $R \sim \text{Poisson}(0.1t)$,
$$E(R) = 0.1t, \quad V(R) = 0.1t.$$
Hence
$$E(R^2) = V(R) + (E(R))^2 = 0.1t + 0.01t^2.$$

(b) The expected daily cost is
$$E(10t + 30R^2) = 10t + 30E(R^2)$$
$$= 10t + 30(0.1t + 0.01t^2)$$
$$= 13t + 0.3t^2.$$

Solution 9.6

This exercise covers some of the ideas and techniques discussed in Section 2.

(a) For $X \sim G_1(p)$, $P(X \geq k) = q^{k-1}$, from (2.2). So
$$1 - F(x) = P(X \geq x + 1) = q^x.$$
Hence, using (2.4),
$$\mu = E(X) = \sum_{x=0}^{\infty} q^x = \frac{1}{1-q} = \frac{1}{p}.$$
(Note that the summation runs from 0 to ∞, even though $P(X = 0) = 0$.)

(b) For $X \sim G_0(p)$, $1 - F(x) = P(X \geq x + 1)$ is the probability that at least $x + 1$ successful trials occur before a failure. Since the probability of a successful trial is p,
$$1 - F(x) = p^{x+1}.$$
Hence, using (2.4),
$$\mu = E(X) = \sum_{x=0}^{\infty} p^{x+1} = \frac{p}{1-p} = \frac{p}{q}.$$

Solution 9.7

This exercise covers some of the ideas and techniques discussed in Section 3.

(a) The p.g.f. can be rewritten as
$$\Pi(s) = \left(\tfrac{3}{4} + \tfrac{1}{4}s\right)^3,$$
so $X \sim B\left(3, \tfrac{1}{4}\right)$. Hence
$$E(X) = 3 \times \tfrac{1}{4} = \tfrac{3}{4},$$
$$V(X) = 3 \times \tfrac{1}{4} \times \tfrac{3}{4} = \tfrac{9}{16}.$$
(b) This is the p.g.f. of Poisson($4t$), which has mean $4t$ and variance $4t$.

(c) The p.g.f. can be rewritten as
$$\Pi(s) = \frac{\tfrac{9}{11}}{1 - \tfrac{2}{11}s},$$
so $X \sim G_0\left(\tfrac{2}{11}\right)$. Hence
$$E(X) = p/q = \tfrac{2}{11} / \tfrac{9}{11} = \tfrac{2}{9},$$
$$V(X) = p/q^2 = \tfrac{2}{11} / \left(\tfrac{9}{11}\right)^2 = \tfrac{22}{81}.$$
(d) The p.g.f. can be rewritten as
$$\Pi(s) = \left(\frac{\tfrac{5}{8}s}{1 - \tfrac{3}{8}s}\right)^4,$$
so X has a negative binomial distribution with parameters $r = 4$ and $p = \tfrac{5}{8}$, and range $\{4, 5, \ldots\}$. Hence
$$E(X) = \frac{r}{p} = \frac{4}{5/8} = 6.4,$$
$$V(X) = \frac{rq}{p^2} = \frac{4 \times \tfrac{3}{8}}{\left(\tfrac{5}{8}\right)^2} = 3.84.$$

Solution 9.8

This exercise covers some of the ideas and techniques discussed in Section 3.

The p.g.f. of a $G_0(p)$ distribution is
$$\Pi(s) = \frac{q}{1 - ps},$$
so
$$\Pi'(s) = \frac{pq}{(1-ps)^2}, \quad \Pi''(s) = \frac{2p^2q}{(1-ps)^3}.$$
Putting $s = 1$ gives
$$\mu = \Pi'(1) = \frac{pq}{q^2} = \frac{p}{q},$$
$$\sigma^2 = \Pi''(1) + \mu - \mu^2$$
$$= \frac{2p^2q}{q^3} + \frac{p}{q} - \frac{p^2}{q^2}$$
$$= \frac{p^2}{q^2} + \frac{p}{q}$$
$$= \frac{p^2 + pq}{q^2}$$
$$= \frac{p(p + q)}{q^2}$$
$$= \frac{p}{q^2}.$$

Solution 9.9

This exercise covers some of the ideas and techniques discussed in Section 3.

(a) Differentiating the p.g.f. gives
$$\Pi'(s) = \frac{6}{(7 - 4s)^2}, \quad \Pi''(s) = \frac{48}{(7 - 4s)^3}.$$
Therefore
$$\Pi'(1) = \tfrac{6}{9} = \tfrac{2}{3}, \quad \Pi''(1) = \tfrac{48}{27} = \tfrac{16}{9},$$
so
$$\mu = E(X) = \tfrac{2}{3},$$
$$V(X) = \Pi''(1) + \mu - \mu^2$$
$$= \tfrac{16}{9} + \tfrac{2}{3} - \left(\tfrac{2}{3}\right)^2$$
$$= 2.$$
(b) $P(X = 0) = \Pi(0) = \tfrac{5}{7}$.

Solution 9.10

This exercise covers some of the ideas and techniques discussed in Section 3.

The p.g.f. can be written as
$$\Pi(s) = s^4 \times \frac{2}{3 - s} = \Pi_X(s) \times \Pi_Y(s).$$
Hence X is a degenerate random variable that takes the value 4, and Y has the geometric distribution with range $\{0, 1, \ldots\}$ and parameter $\tfrac{1}{3}$. Therefore $Z = 4 + Y$, where $Y \sim G_0\left(\tfrac{1}{3}\right)$.

Alternatively, the p.g.f. can be written as
$$\Pi(s) = s^3 \times \frac{2s}{3 - s}.$$
Then $Z = 3 + W$, where $W \sim G_1\left(\tfrac{2}{3}\right)$.

Solution 9.11

This exercise covers some of the ideas and techniques discussed in Section 4.

(a) The total area under the p.d.f. is 1, so
$$k \int_1^2 (2 - x)\, dx = k\left[2x - \tfrac{1}{2}x^2\right]_1^2 = \tfrac{1}{2}k = 1.$$
Therefore $k = 2$.

(b) The mean of X is
$$E(X) = \int_{-\infty}^{\infty} x\, f(x)\, dx$$
$$= \int_1^2 \left(4x - 2x^2\right) dx$$
$$= \left[2x^2 - \tfrac{2}{3}x^3\right]_1^2$$
$$= 1\tfrac{1}{3}.$$
Similarly,
$$E\left(X^2\right) = \int_1^2 \left(4x^2 - 2x^3\right) dx$$
$$= \left[\tfrac{4}{3}x^3 - \tfrac{1}{2}x^4\right]_1^2$$
$$= 1\tfrac{5}{6},$$
so
$$V(X) = E\left(X^2\right) - \mu^2 = 1\tfrac{5}{6} - \left(1\tfrac{1}{3}\right)^2 = \tfrac{1}{18}.$$

(c) For $1 \le x \le 2$,
$$F(x) = \int_1^x (4 - 2u)\, du$$
$$= \left[4u - u^2\right]_1^x$$
$$= 4x - x^2 - 3.$$
Hence
$$F(x) = \begin{cases} 0, & x < 1, \\ 4x - x^2 - 3, & 1 \le x \le 2, \\ 1, & x > 2. \end{cases}$$

(d) $P(X \ge 1.5) = 1 - F(1.5) = 1 - 0.75 = 0.25$,
$$P(1.2 < X < 1.6) = F(1.6) - F(1.2)$$
$$= 0.84 - 0.36$$
$$= 0.48.$$

Solution 9.12

This exercise covers some of the ideas and techniques discussed in Sections 4 and 6.

(a) The proportion of customers that the shop assistant takes more than five minutes to serve is given by
$$1 - F(5) = 1 - \left(1 - \tfrac{4}{25}\right) = 0.16.$$

(b) Using (4.4),
$$E(T) = \int_0^{\infty} (1 - F(t))\, dt$$
$$= \int_0^2 1\, dt + \int_2^{\infty} \frac{4}{t^2}\, dt$$
$$= 2 + \left[-\frac{4}{t}\right]_2^{\infty}$$
$$= 2 + 2 = 4 \text{ minutes.}$$

(c) Given $u = 0.653\,25$, the simulated time t is the solution of
$$F(t) = 0.653\,25,$$
that is,
$$1 - \frac{4}{t^2} = 0.653\,25.$$
This gives
$$t = 3.396\,42\ldots \text{ minutes} \simeq 3 \text{ minutes } 24 \text{ seconds.}$$

Solution 9.13

This exercise covers some of the ideas and techniques discussed in Sections 4 and 6.

(a) The probability required is
$$P(T > 5) = \frac{8}{5^3} = 0.064.$$

(b) The median time m satisfies $F(m) = \tfrac{1}{2}$. The c.d.f. of T is
$$F(t) = P(T \le t) = 1 - \frac{8}{t^3},$$
so m is the solution of
$$1 - \frac{8}{m^3} = \tfrac{1}{2}.$$
Therefore
$$m^3 = 16,$$
and hence $m \simeq 2.520$ minutes or 2 minutes 31 seconds.

(c) Using the alternative formula for the mean (4.4),
$$E(T) = \int_0^{\infty} (1 - F(t))\, dt$$
$$= \int_0^2 1\, dt + \int_2^{\infty} \frac{8}{t^3}\, dt$$
$$= 2 + \left[-\frac{4}{t^2}\right]_2^{\infty}$$
$$= 3 \text{ minutes.}$$

(d) The p.d.f. of T is

$$f(t) = F'(t) = \frac{24}{t^4}, \quad t > 2.$$

So

$$E(T^2) = \int_2^\infty t^2 \times \frac{24}{t^4} \, dt$$

$$= \int_2^\infty \frac{24}{t^2} \, dt$$

$$= \left[-\frac{24}{t} \right]_2^\infty$$

$$= 12,$$

and hence

$$V(T) = 12 - 3^2 = 3 \text{ (minutes)}^2.$$

(e) Given a random number u from $U(0,1)$, the corresponding simulated time t (in minutes) is the solution of $F(t) = u$, so the first simulated time is the solution of

$$1 - \frac{8}{t^3} = 0.264.$$

This gives

$$t^3 = \frac{8}{1 - 0.264} = 10.869\ldots,$$

and hence

$$t = 2.215\ldots \text{ minutes} \simeq 2 \text{ minutes } 13 \text{ seconds}.$$

Similarly, using the other three random numbers gives the following three simulated times:
2 minutes 5 seconds, 2 minutes 38 seconds and
3 minutes 33 seconds.

Solution 9.14

This exercise covers some of the ideas and techniques discussed in Section 5.

(a) By the memoryless property, the distribution of the time T_i until a bus on route i arrives is exponential with mean μ_i, where $\mu_1 = 5$, $\mu_2 = 5$ and $\mu_3 = 10$. Therefore $T_1 \sim M\left(\frac{1}{5}\right)$, $T_2 \sim M\left(\frac{1}{5}\right)$, $T_3 \sim M\left(\frac{1}{10}\right)$. The time T that I will have to wait for a bus to arrive is the minimum of T_1, T_2 and T_3, so

$$T \sim M\left(\tfrac{1}{5} + \tfrac{1}{5} + \tfrac{1}{10}\right) = M\left(\tfrac{1}{2}\right).$$

(b) The probability that I will have to wait more than 10 minutes for a bus is

$$P(T > 10) = e^{-\frac{1}{2} \times 10} = e^{-5} \simeq 0.0067.$$

(c) The probability that I will have to wait less than 20 seconds for a bus is

$$P\left(T < \tfrac{1}{3}\right) = 1 - e^{-\frac{1}{2} \times \frac{1}{3}}$$

$$= 1 - e^{-1/6}$$

$$\simeq 0.1535.$$

Solution 9.15

This exercise covers some of the ideas and techniques discussed in Section 6.

(a) One possible scheme using single digits is given in Table S.7.

Table S.7 A simulation scheme

Digit	Outcome
0, 1	Dies
2, 3, 4, 5, 6, 7	Survives
8, 9	Ignore (take next digit)

(b) One possible scheme using pairs of digits is given in Table S.8.

Table S.8 Another simulation scheme

Digits	Outcome
01, ..., 25	Dies
26, ..., 99, 00	Survives

Solution 9.16

This exercise covers some of the ideas and techniques discussed in Section 6.

(a) Values of the p.m.f. and c.d.f. of Poisson(1.6) are given in Table S.9.

Table S.9 Values of the p.m.f. and c.d.f. of Poisson(1.6)

x	0	1	2	3	$\cdots$
$p(x)$	0.2019	0.3230	0.2584	0.1378	$\cdots$
$F(x)$	0.2019	0.5249	0.7833	0.9211	$\cdots$

Since

$$F(0) < 0.2690 \leq F(1),$$

the first simulated value is $x_1 = 1$. Since $0.0191 \leq F(0)$, the second simulated value is $x_2 = 0$. Similarly, the third simulated value is $x_3 = 3$.

(b) Values from $M(1.6)$ can be obtained by multiplying the values from $M(1)$ by the mean of $M(1.6)$, that is by multiplying them by $1/1.6 = 0.625$ (or, equivalently, by dividing them by 1.6). This gives $x_1 = 0.3475$ and $x_2 = 1.96$.

(c) Since $\mu = 7$ and $\sigma = \sqrt{100} = 10$, for each number z from $N(0,1)$, an observation from $N(7, 100)$ can be simulated by calculating $x = 10z + 7$. The two simulated observations are

$$x_1 = 10 \times 0.9982 + 7 = 16.982,$$

$$x_2 = 10 \times -1.6920 + 7 = -9.92.$$

Index